MAN, MEMORY, AND MACHINES

AN INTRODUCTION TO CYBERNETICS

Man, Memory

AN INTRODUCTION

Illustrated with photographs, drawings, and diagrams

and Machines

TO CYBERNETICS

by Corinne Jacker

THE MACMILLAN COMPANY, NEW YORK
COLLIER-MACMILLAN LIMITED, LONDON

LIBRARY OF CONGRESS CATALOG CARD NUMBER: 64–11764

DESIGNED BY MARGERY KRONENGOLD

THE MACMILLAN COMPANY, NEW YORK
COLLIER-MACMILLAN CANADA, LTD., TORONTO, ONTARIO

PRINTED IN THE UNITED STATES OF AMERICA

TO THE MEMORY OF
Carl Howard Litvin

Contents

List of Illustrations

Preface

FOR CENTURIES man has been haunted by machines his imagination has created, machines that can think, act on their own, and in the end could even rule and destroy mankind. In folklore and literature this idea occurs again and again. But today it is not necessary to read science fiction to learn about strange machines. It is possible to pick up the newspaper or listen to television and find factual accounts of mechanisms more miraculous than any our ancestors dreamed of: electronic animals that "feed," learn, and respond like mice, tortoises, rats, and other creatures; computers that play chess and checkers, write poetry and music, and even design other computers.

These creations and many more are largely the result of the new science of cybernetics, which deals not only with machines, but with the human brain and nervous system—with the way in which man thinks, reacts, behaves, and learns. Indeed, cybernetics has shown how much man has in common with the machines he has made.

The practical applications of this new science are powerfully affecting our world. Oil refineries are operated and controlled entirely by computers, soldiers aim computer-guided weapons into the sky, satellites zoom into orbit along paths calculated by the computers that control them, doctors consult a computer about the proper diagnosis of a heart ailment. This book, however, will concentrate on the story behind cybernetics, its origins, and some of the ideas and theories of this exciting new field.

Modern man is living in an age of invention and exploration so different and startling that it has inspired some people to call it the "Second Industrial Revolution." This is because, just as the power-driven tools of the mid-eighteenth century completely changed the economy and culture of their time, so the advances of cybernetics have brought us to the threshold of a new era.

CORINNE JACKER

MAN, MEMORY, AND MACHINES

AN INTRODUCTION TO CYBERNETICS

*It must always be remembered that man's body is what it is
through having been moulded into its present shape
by the chances and changes of many millions of years, but
that his organisation never advanced with anything like
the rapidity with which that of the machine is advancing.*

SAMUEL BUTLER, *Erewhon* (1872)

1

Cybernetics:
"Steersman" of a New Age

LIKE MANY UPRISINGS, the cybernetic revolution began quite quietly. It was started in Cambridge, Massachusetts, in the late 1930's by a group of scientists who met once a month under the guidance of the Mexican physician, Dr. Arturo Rosenblueth, to discuss the scientific method. The *scientific method* is a way of approaching the physical world in a logical, objective, and systematic way in order to find out what it is like and how it functions. To these lively and informal discussions came the American mathematician, Norbert Wiener, who is called the "father of cybernetics."

Dr. Weiner and Dr. Rosenblueth found that they had much in common. Both were interested in the unexplored border areas between the specialized scientific fields. Here, where the separate sciences are related or even overlap, lies the possibility of again unifying them. Man has recently been learning so much about the world around him that it is becoming harder all the time to know more than a little of the vast information that is accumulating. Scientists and other scholars usually concentrate on one area so that they can learn it thoroughly, but this means that they also tend to learn less and less about other fields. People who travel to foreign countries frequently have trouble in making themselves understood when they can only speak one language. In the same way scientists have trouble when they try to travel into another scientific field. A biologist may talk about his work using one kind of technical language, a chemist—talking about the same general area—will use another, and a physiologist yet a third.

This difference in the way scientists approach a problem and in the words they use to describe it has meant that basic work that may be much the same in several sciences has been done over again a number of times; and because of the sharp divisions among the sciences, important work has been held up because men in one field did not know about vital discoveries made in another. Dr. Rosenblueth and others felt that in order to explore the frontiers of science effectively it would be necessary to have teams of scientists who were experts in their own field and also familiar with the language and concepts of their colleagues.

World War II created the first real need for these teams, and it also supplied the opportunity to organize them. As these teams of scientists from different fields worked on problems, they found that, for example, the way in which some machines regulate themselves is similar to certain activities of the animal nervous system. Men who were studying the human brain found that they could learn much from communications theory, which had been developed by engineers and mathematicians. From this early work during and after the war years, the ideas of Dr. Wiener and his co-workers grew, and in 1948 Wiener published the book that named—and for the first time in book

Four pioneers of cybernetics. LEFT TO RIGHT: *W. Ross Ashby, Warren McCulloch, Grey Walter, and Norbert Wiener. (Courtesy Philippe Constantin)*

form described—this new science. His book was called *Cybernetics: or Control and Communication in the Animal and the Machine.*

The term "cybernetics" is derived from the Greek *kubernetes,* meaning "steersman," and our word "governor" comes from a Latin version of this same Greek word. The name was coined for two major reasons. The first scientific paper contributing directly to the ideas behind this field—published in 1868 by the British physicist James Clerk Maxwell (1831–1879)—was called "The Theory of Governors," and dealt with self-regulating or *feedback* mechanisms. These had been named "governors" by the Scottish inventor of the steam engine, James Watt (1736–1819). The second reason for choosing the term "cybernetics" was that the steering mechanism on a ship is one of the best examples of a feedback mechanism.

It is possible to understand what feedback is by looking at one of the most common examples of such a mechanism, the ordinary household thermostat. This simple device is used to keep room temperature at a constant pre-set level. Suppose you want to keep the temperature in your living room at about 70 degrees during the winter months, and you set your thermostat accordingly. If the temperature goes down to, say, 65 degrees, information reaches the thermostat that the room is too cold. This is called the *input.* The thermostat then "consults" its instructions, which are, in effect, "if the temperature in the living room falls below 70 degrees, start the furnace." It then activates the furnace, which begins to burn fuel in order to raise the room temperature; this is the *output.*

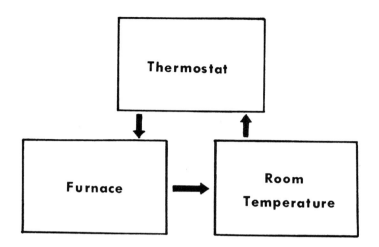

The feedback loop.

But the thermostat is always alert; if the room becomes too warm and the temperature climbs above 70 degrees, it receives this information, too, and immediately turns off the furnace.

The diagram shows what the so-called *feedback loop* is. The three elements, including the variable that is supposed to be controlled—the room temperature, are all interdependent on one another. They form a *closed system*, because the operation of the system does not depend on any other elements; and the system is *self-regulating*—adjusting and controlling itself. It is the temperature of the room that determines whether the furnace will be in operation or not, and whether or not the furnace operates determines the temperature of the room. A feedback mechanism is, as the English mathematician Charles Babbage (1792–1871) said, capable of "eating its own tail."

Information has been communicated, and in accordance with that information the system has responded with an action that regulates itself. It is by this "steering" process that the thermostat or any other feedback system works. If information is communicated in this way in both animal and machine, the study of the feedback system and its control could be applicable to men as well as machines.

2

Brains and Computers

BY FINDING some common ground between the biological and physical sciences—between the nervous system and electronics—it has also been possible to describe certain electronic devices and the brain within the same frame of reference and in much the same terms. So today electrical engineers talk about the memory of machines, and biologists and psychologists describe certain human conditions in terms of feedback.

Man's brain has long been regarded with wonder and awe. Unique among the animals, he has used his mind to learn to reason; to count and speak; to create works of art, whole cities, and great scientific marvels—including "electronic brains." But now, cybernetic studies show that this great human gift has much in common with the modern computer. Indeed, some people have gone so far as to refer to the brain as simply an organic computer, a feedback system with *neurons*—nerve cells—using, like the vacuum tubes in the computer, electrical impulses to operate and instruct the body.

For more than a hundred and fifty years it has been known that there is an electrical aspect to the interaction of the nerves and muscles of the body. This very important area of biological study is called bioelectricity or *electrophysiology*; it was formally begun in the year 1791.

At that time the Italian physiologist Luigi Galvani (1737–1798) published his theory of animal electricity. In the 1780's Galvani, with the assistance of his wife Lucia, began performing some experiments on frogs.

The Galvanis took dissected frogs and observed the action of *electricity* on the muscles of the animals' legs. A bronze hook (bronze is an alloy of copper and tin) was attached to the frog's body, and the frog was placed on an iron railing. When a leg touched the railing it jerked suddenly in a spasm of movement. An electrical current had flowed through the completed circuit (the frog connecting the bronze and iron), thus making a very primitive battery. Although Galvani did not realize the mechanical importance of his discovery, his friend, the physicist Alessandro Volta (1745–1827), did and in the early years of the nineteenth century constructed the first successful battery.

Galvani, who continued to devote himself to his physiological research, discovered two very important things during his frog experiments. First, animal tissues, such as nerves and muscles, are very good conductors of electrical current. Second, when an electrical current flows along the body from the nervous system to the muscles, action results.

This was the first inkling of the human electrical feedback system.

Almost sixty years after this pioneering work, in 1848, the great German physicist and physiologist Hermann von Helmholtz (1821–1894) discovered just how fast a frog transmits nerve impulses. He found that such an electrical impulse travels along the frog's nervous system at the rate of about 65 miles per hour. It is now known that the speed with which the impulse travels depends on such things as the size of the nerve cell and on the temperature of the cell when it is conducting the current. (A more complete discussion of this fascinating subject appears in *Nerves and Muscles* by the American neurophysiologist Robert Galambos.)

Shortly thereafter it became known that the brain emits waves of electrical current, and in 1875 the first animal *brain waves* were recorded. But this field was not investigated very thoroughly until the second quarter of this century; it may be that adequate equipment was just not available until that time.

Finally in 1929 an Austrian doctor, Hans Berger, developed the first practical and successful device to register and record brain waves. It was called the *electroencephalograph* (*EEG*), and is now an essential tool of modern medicine.

Since 1929 an enormous number of brain-wave records have been made, and the usual pattern of the brain has by now become apparent. When an infant's brain waves are recorded, the EEG shows jumbled and confused highs and lows, with no real rhythmic pattern. Slowly, the waves settle into an orderly and rhythmical progression. In early youth between four and seven pulses of electricity per second are recorded, and this number gradually increases until ten pulses per second become the usual emission. This number of pulses is called the *alpha rhythm*, and is the typical pattern of an adult mind when the body is at rest and the subject not thinking of anything in particular. Scientists have now found that the number of pulses recorded by an EEG changes very noticeably when the person being tested is learning something.

The "biological computer" of the human brain has as its major elements the nerve cells, or neurons. A neuron is a very intricate structure; a typical one is composed of a central cell body from which come many filaments, called *dendrites,* and one *axon.* The stimulus, or electrical pulse, enters the nerve cell through the dendrites; this is the input. Then the cell fires, that is, it transmits an electrical pulse of its own. This electrical impulse travels along the axon (the output) to the *synapse*—the point at which it is transmitted to the next neuron.

Throughout the nineteenth century scientists believed that the nerve emitted a varying amount of electrical current. They pictured the nervous system as operating like a water faucet, each cell being capable of being turned on partially or all the way, depending on the stimulus. But at the beginning of this century it was learned that the nerve either fires or is at rest.

This characteristic can be described in the terms an electronic engineer would use in talking about an electrical current. Electricity is, like the electrical pulses of the neuron, an all-or-nothing substance. It is on, or it is off; electrical

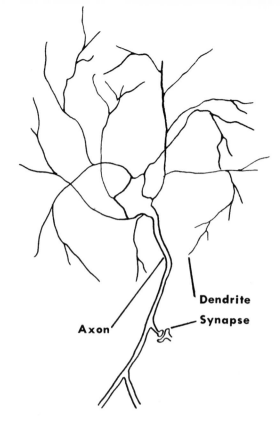

Dendrite

Synapse

Axon

A *neuron*.

current flows, or it does not flow. And it is because of this that the neuron is compared to *vacuum tubes* or *transistors* (the tiny devices that can act like vacuum tubes) as they are used in *electronic computers*. And, from the information translated by these electrical impulses of the nervous system come our actions, thoughts, perhaps even our emotions.

Nerve cells gather and store energy, becoming "storage batteries" that operate on an energy supply of oxygen and sugar. The outside of a nerve fiber at rest has a positive electrical charge, and this has a significant effect on the transmission of electricity. To see clearly just what this means, it is necessary to understand something about the atom.

An *atom* is the smallest particle of an *element* (the basic substances of which the universe is made, such as oxygen, sodium, or lead) to retain all the physical and chemical properties of that element. The atom has a nucleus, which contains *neutrons* (particles with no electrical charge) and *protons* (particles with a positive electrical charge). Whirling around the nucleus, much the way the planets of our solar system revolve around the sun, are *electrons* (particles with a negative electrical charge). Particles with the same electrical charge repel one another; when particles have opposite electrical charges they attract one another.

An ordinary storage battery, or dry cell, has two poles, one positive (marked +) and the other negative (marked −). When an electric circuit is completed, electrons flow from the negative pole toward the positive pole. A flow of electrons is called an electric current, or, sometimes, a negative electric current. It is known that similarly an electric current flows through the neuron, but the exact process is not yet completely understood.

Although the transmission of electrical impulses is very important in the functioning of the neuron, it is not the only vital aspect. The impulses that the nervous system transmits are the result of very complex chemical reactions involving electrically charged particles called *ions*, which can carry either a positive or a negative charge.

Electronic computers have control centers; so, too, the very complex operations of the nervous system have a control center in the brain. Signals come into the brain from all the sense organs, each sense organ transmitting its stimuli along different kinds of nerve fibers. In the brain the *cortex* is the area where the impulses are sorted and routed to the special areas dealing with that particular sense. Here they are analyzed, decisions are made, and the answering pulse returns along the nervous system.

The tremendous tasks the human brain performs every moment become clear when one realizes that every sensation—perception of color, light, sound, heat, cold, pain, and so on—is transmitted by electrical impulses. It is one of the miracles of nature that almost always the animal nervous system is equipped to send the right information to the right section of the brain. Imagine the confusion if when a light was turned on suddenly you "heard" it, or if upon hearing the first notes of "The Star-Spangled Banner" you saw the colors green and yellow.

One of the most precious possessions a human being has is his memory. Not only does this faculty enable him to learn and function as he must in this world, but it provides each person with recollections of his own individual and unique past. Memories, in order to exist, must be stored somewhere. The amount of information that the brain is capable of storing must be fantastically great. Available when wanted are names to go with familiar faces, the word "chair" associated with that four-legged object on which one sits, and the events of a very happy or sad day.

Very little is known about memory or its nature. What it is, how it exists, and where the individual bits of information are stored simply is not known. But we are beginning to get some inklings about this mysterious phenomenon.

Imagine yourself in the observation balcony of an operating room. The harsh lights glare down on a solemn group of doctors and nurses. They are gathered around the patient, who lies awake with his eyes closed, under a local anesthetic. There is a hush as the surgeon stares down at him before beginning the operation. The patient's head is shaved and sterilized. He is very ill, a violent kind of epilepsy has given him very severe and frequent seizures, and the doctor is trying to destroy the tissues in the part of the brain where the epileptic seizures originate.

Through a minute hole that he has drilled in the patient's skull, the doctor inserts an *electrode*, a thin metal device with a needlelike point. The electrode is connected to a source of electricity and conducts an electrical current. The doctor, knowing the electrical nature of epilepsy, is using the electrode to find precisely the area concerned.

Suddenly the man on the operating table begins to hum a part of the tune "Night and Day." The startled doctor pulls back the electrode for a moment, and the patient is quiet. But, as soon as the electrode comes in contact with the brain, he begins to hum again! And not even at a different part of the tune; instead he begins exactly where he did the first time. Every time the electrode is removed, the humming stops. As soon as it touches the same spot in the brain, the song begins again.

The doctor moves the electrode to another area of the brain, and his patient begins to talk, not to the doctor, but to someone else, someone not in the operating room. The man is experiencing some episode in his past. As he will say later, it is *as if* he were actually there. Again, no matter at what point the story is interrupted by the removal of the electrode, as soon as contact is established again the patient, instead of continuing to experience the event, goes back to where he first began.

This is not the story of the latest science-fiction movie. Events like these have actually occurred. This is like many that took place in an operating room in the Montreal Neurological Institute; the surgeon was Dr. Wilder Penfield. Dr. Penfield is a pioneer in the exploration of the human memory and sensation. He has found that the same pattern is followed in every case where a certain area of the brain is stimulated in such a way that a memory becomes "present" again. Each memory seems to be played, like the reel on a tape recorder, that is run to a certain point, stopped, rewound, and played over again.

Somewhere in the human nervous system there may be a "library" of past experience, a memory storage unit. But the question is, where can all the records be kept? If a person sat down and started to write all the memories stored in his head, it would take months or even years to finish the job (that is, assuming total recall, or the ability to remember everything).

A clue to the puzzle may be found in recent discoveries in the field of genetics, the study of heredity. Certain patterns or traits are passed on from one generation to another. A chicken's offspring are chickens, not ducks or geese. Moreover, special traits also are transmitted; two curly-haired parents usually have a curly-haired child.

The way these blueprints of life are passed on from

parent to child has long been one of the most intriguing mysteries of reproduction. Parents have looked at their infant sons or daughters and marveled at the perfection of each part of the small body; children growing up echo visual and personality traits of their parents or grandparents. And yet, everyone is different, no two persons are exactly alike.

Now two scientists have found the answer to this riddle. The Englishman Francis Crick and the American James Watson worked together at Cambridge University in England. They found the blueprint in the giant protein molecule of *deoxyribonucleic acid* (DNA). *Molecules* are made up of atoms linked together by a sharing of electrons. The DNA molecule is composed of two chains of atoms wound together in a double helix, or double spiral.

There are four chemical bases in every DNA molecule. They are adenine (A), guanine (G), thymine (T), and cytosine (C). These four bases can be arranged in a vast number of sequences and combinations. The way in which they are arranged is the genetic code, the instructions for the blueprint of a living creature; and it is exactly

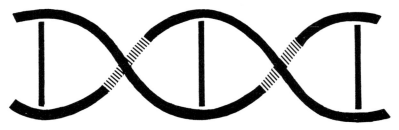

A model of a DNA molecule.

a code, a series of information-giving symbols. The sequence for a dog might be CAAAGGTTCA; that for a walrus, GGGGGTAAACTTTTCAG. Because of the genetic code, a man is a human and not a horse, but he is not the same human as his father.

In human DNA, the code probably consists of a sequence of billions of combinations of the four bases. In this way instructions are given for growth, hair color, eye color, and for all the specialized tissues forming the muscles, nerves, and other cells of the human body. All of this information is packed into the infinitesimally small DNA molecule.

It has been suggested by some that memory is recorded in a similar code. Perhaps all of a person's past, all he has learned, is encoded by the electrical impulses of neurons into stored molecules. The American science writer John Pfeiffer, in his book *The Human Brain*, reports some interesting experiments that throw light on this area.

The Swedish biologist Holgar Hyden has been studying the learning power of rats. He observed the chemical changes in their bodies as they learn to balance themselves on a seesaw. While the rats are "studying" and adjusting their bodies in order to learn how to balance, a very interesting bodily change takes place, involving another heredity-related giant protein molecule, *ribonucleic acid* (RNA). In the rats' nerve cells during learning there is a substantial increase in the amount of RNA; and it is known that RNA carries complex, coded hereditary information, like DNA. It is possible that RNA molecules can also encode and retain learned information—that they can, in effect, be programmed.

In support of this idea, Dr. Hyden has observed that when the learning process is over and the rats can balance more or less successfully, the level of RNA in the nerve cells drops back into its normal range. But, in the nearby non-neural cells, the RNA level rises. It may be that these cells are the "memory bank" science is searching for.

It has been shown, for example, in the discussion of bio-electricity, that it is profitable to talk about organic systems in terms usually used to describe inorganic processes. But another element is needed if the brain is to be talked about in cybernetic terms. Cybernetics deals with communication in animals and machines; it also deals with control—with self-regulating systems—and it may be valuable to talk about the human or animal nervous system in terms of feedback.

In Chapter 1 one of the simplest feedback mechanisms was discussed; this was the thermostat. The human body, too, has a thermostat of a sort that controls and regulates body temperature, keeping it within certain rather narrow limits no matter what the outside temperature may be. This has been called one of the most important evolutionary advantages that warm-blooded animals have. The human thermostat is in the *hypothalamus*, a vital area of the brain and one of the most important human control centers.

Suppose that on a hot summer day, after being outside in 90-degree temperatures you go into an air-conditioned movie theater, where the thermometer reads about 70 degrees, as much to cool off as to see the show. As soon as the cold air reaches the skin, its temperature—the body's surface temperature—begins to drop. Nerve fibers in the skin's sense organs immediately start flashing this important message to the brain in their on-off code. When the information reaches the hypothalamus it is evaluated, and instructions are sent out to set the necessary plan of operation into effect. Signals are sent to the heart and blood vessels with instructions to alter the flow of blood pumped into the vessels at the surface of the skin, and the body temperature rises. When it is at its proper level, the hypothalamus, which has been receiving information about the temperature, sends signals to the necessary parts of the body that will result in actions necessary to keep the body temperature constant. As the temperature of the body fluctuates, the ever-alert hypothalamus signals corrective measures, keeping it always on an even keel.

Certain aspects of the brain have been compared to those of a computer. But this is not to say that those who argue that humans and computers are pretty much on a level with each other are correct. Behind the story of cybernetics (and of electronic computers and all machines) is the human story, the struggle for knowledge and wisdom. A man invented the first computer. No computer has yet invented a man.

Blaise Pascal (1623–1662). (The Bettmann Archive)

3

The Background
of Cybernetics

A SCIENCE IS—at least in part—built on the experiments, ideas, and suggestions of the past. Man plans his future and constructs his present on the solid foundation that generations of great men have laid. Cybernetics, too, has roots that go far back in time.

Thousands of years ago a primitive man built the first calculating machine when he moved a pebble from one pile to another as a way of counting. From this to the abacus—the Chinese calculating machine that works by moving beads along wires—and to the electronic computer was a slow, painful journey along the centuries.

Perhaps the first calculating machine directly related to cybernetics was built in France in 1642. There a very intelligent and bored young man was working in his father's Paris tax office. This young man, the philosopher and mathematician Blaise Pascal (1623–1662), felt that he was wasting his time in continually adding long columns of figures. Blaise felt that such ordinary, humdrum, and boring labor should be done at least in part by machines. And so he did something about the problem: he constructed an adding machine. Pascal's computer was able to add numbers up to the hundreds of thousands or—said in another way—to six columns of figures. For example, the number shown in the illustration is 338,398. If the next number to be added were 2, Pascal would have moved the unit column indicator (far right) two notches. This would have brought the circular toothed gear inside the box that registered the units full circle to 0 again, and would have moved the next gear (the tens) one notch. Since it already is at 9, the one notch brings this gear, too, to 0 and moves the next gear (the hundreds) one notch to 4. So the next number to appear would be 338,400. Pascal's labor saver is the forerunner of our modern mechanically operated desk-top adding machines.

A few years later the great German mathematician and philosopher Gottfried Wilhelm Leibniz (1646–1716) exhibited a calculating machine of his own design to the Academy of Paris and the Royal Society of London. This was a vast improvement on Pascal's calculator; it could multiply, divide, and extract roots of numbers as well as adding and subtracting them.

Leibniz was also interested in problems of communication, the transmission of information between man and man, man and machine, or between machine and machine. Norbert Wiener has said that in many ways Leibniz is the intellectual ancestor of cybernetics. Among the aspects of the theory of communication that Leibniz developed or originated were the idea of a universal scientific language (you will remember how important this was to the modern founders of cybernetics) and a *Calculus Ratiocinator*. This calculus of logic was the forerunner of one of the most important tools of cybernetics: mathematical, or symbolic, logic, which is the use of mathematical symbols to convey logical ideas, and the manipulation of language according to the methods and rules of mathematics.

Another strange fact is that Leibniz philosophically considered the binary (two-element) system of numbers used

Pascal's calculator. (The Bettmann Archive)

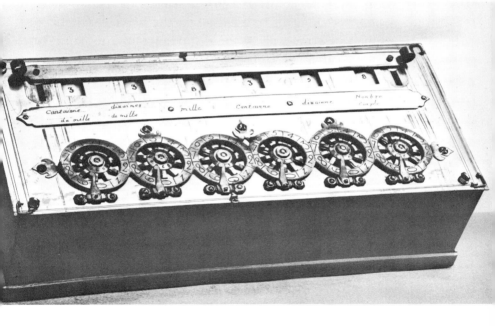

by electronic computers (see Chapter 4). For Leibniz the numeral 1 represented God, and 0 nothingness, or the void out of which the world was created.

In the nineteenth century, scientists began to learn more about how the body functions. And in 1817, about twenty-five years after Galvani published the results of his experiments with frogs showing the presence of animal electricity, the French physiologist François Magendie (1783–1855) published one of the first discussions of the principle of feedback and control in the animal. To Magendie, a *reflex action* was an activity caused by a disturbance (input) in some part of the body. Information about this disturbance traveled along the central nervous system to the brain, the point of control. Here, instructions were issued, which again traveled along the nervous system, to respond in some way to the disturbance, the response be-

Leibniz' calculating machine.
(*The Bettmann Archive*)

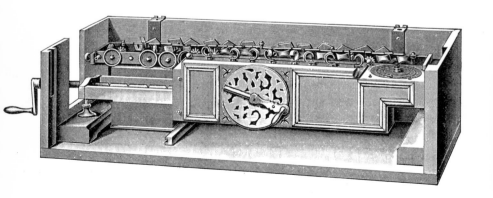

ing the output. The most extensive work on reflex actions was done in the early years of this century by the Russian physiologist Ivan Pavlov (1849–1936), and since that time psychologists and physiologists have been pursuing this subject.

The nineteenth century was not only a time of great excitement and discovery in the pure sciences; it was, in its early years, the peak of the first Industrial Revolution, the result of discoveries in the applied sciences. Many advances in science and technology have been made because ambitious and practical men were seeking a cheaper and more efficient way of doing something. The silk-weaving industry in France was suffering because the looms necessary for the weaving of brocaded silk were cumbersome, and required so many man-hours that the costs of these brocades were becoming prohibitive.

The French inventor Joseph Marie Jacquard (1752–1834) became very interested in this problem. In 1801 he exhibited a loom that used a series of cards with holes punched in them according to the desired pattern. The whole card could be perforated, thus allowing every needle in the loom to go through it to the threads, or a pattern of holes could be punched in the card allowing only the needles for that particular row in the pattern to go through, or no holes could be punched in the card so that no needles could reach the threads. For every new step in the pattern a new card would have to be used.

Just as modern workers worry about the security of their jobs when a factory is automated, the French silk weavers opposed the introduction of the Jacquard looms, but they had no success, and the looms introduced a new prosperity to the weaving industry of France. The punched cards of the IBM (International Business Machines) computers and of other electronic calculators have as their "grandfather" the pattern card of the Jacquard loom.

A few years later, in about 1812, one of the great pioneers of automatic computing machines began to think about a calculator. The English mathematician and inventor, Charles Babbage (1792–1871), was very concerned with mathematical accuracy. At this time astronomical and mathematical tables were being constructed by scientists without the aid of machines. No matter how accurate these men tried to be, errors crept into the tables, making them difficult or impossible to use. Babbage wanted to invent a machine that would eliminate all chance of human error, and calculate and print mathematical tables. He called his machine the "Difference Engine."

Charles Babbage
(1792–1871).
(The Bettmann Archive)

A *small part* of Babbage's *Difference Engine.*
(*The Bettmann Archive*)

Babbage's idea seemed a very practical one, and he succeeded in interesting the English government in his work, thus receiving some financial help. In 1823 he began what was to be many years of work on the Difference Engine. But when, after spending a great deal of money and time, Babbage still had not finished his machine, the government withdrew its support. Finally, in 1833, Babbage abandoned all his plans for the Difference Engine. This was not because he was discouraged; rather, he wanted to be free to concentrate on an even more elaborate calculator, the first modern computer!

This calculator, which used Jacquard-type punched cards, was called the Analytical Engine; and it is the machine to which Babbage referred when he said it would be capable of "eating its own tail." For the first time in history, Babbage was planning a calculator that could control itself and that would work by feedback. The "mill," which was to perform the mathematical work that had been programmed on the punched cards, would feed back to itself the answers to simple mathematical problems it had solved in order to solve more complex ones. It was to be a kind of "learning machine." But at Babbage's death this great invention had not been completed; and, although he left his plans and partially finished equipment to the Science Museum in London, it never was finished.

Babbage's Analytical Engine is important not only because it was the first modern computer, but because it also shows us a very vital aspect of cybernetics. Since the modern computer operates by electrical power, and the feedback mechanism of the human nervous system is in part electrical in nature, many people assume that electricity is theoretically necessary for the operation of a self-regulating control system. This is not so. Babbage's Engine was purely mechanical in its operation, and when it was completed it would not have required any kind of electrical power.

Babbage's machine encouraged men to ask a question they are still asking. Can machines think? When faced with chess-playing computers, machines that are learning to perceive letters of the alphabet, and other strange electronic marvels, many of us are chilled at the thought of a whole generation of "Frankenstein monsters." To many the whole idea of a thinking machine challenges their firm belief in the superiority of humans. The late British logician A. M. Turing, who has said that machines certainly are capable of thought, mentions a memoir by Lady Lovelace, a contemporary of Babbage. Lady Lovelace said, "The Analytical Engine has no pretensions to *originate* anything. It can do *whatever we know how to order it* to perform."

People still feel that this distinction between creative thought—originating an idea and following it through to a conclusion—and "thinking" along the lines of a completely instructed program is a safe one to make and excludes computers from the realm of thought. On the other hand, there is the statement of the Spanish inventor of a chess-playing machine, Leonardo Torres y Quevedo, who said, "The limits within which thought is really necessary need to be better defined. . . . The automaton can do many things that are popularly classed as thought."

4

Yes or No: How the Computer Counts and Reasons

THE STORY of how man learned to count is buried in the distant past, thousands of years before written records of any kind existed. At some time in man's history a great intellectual leap was made. Exactly how we do not know; perhaps a primitive man was looking at the food he had collected for storing against the winter. He knew that there were "many" or at any rate "more than one" individual items. Suddenly, a marvelous idea occurred to him. His hands, which had labored to gather his food, were two ready-made calculating machines. By holding up or touching one finger for each item in the piles of food before him, he could find a way to say how many things there were. The fruit he had saved might equal all the fingers on one hand plus the thumb of the other; the pile of nuts might have as many nuts in it as he had fingers on both hands and toes on both feet.

This concept that the number of things there are is independent of what kinds of things are counted—a group of nine apples and a group of nine eggs have in common only that there are nine things in each group—is one of the most important man ever arrived at.

Our word *digit*—any number under ten—comes from the Latin *digitus*, which means "finger." In fact, the German historian and archaeologist Theodor Mommsen (1817–1903) was struck by the visual significance of the lower Roman numerals. I (or 1 in our numerical system) might clearly be a symbol for one finger held up; V (or 5) could be a kind of pictorial representation of an open hand held with the thumb spread far apart from the fingers. Then X (10) would be two of these.

Our numerical system, the *decimal system*, has a *base* of 10. A base is the number on which a mathematical system is constructed—its basis—and in the digital system all mathematical operations are based on the number 10. It may be that we have chosen this base because there are ten fingers (including the thumbs) on our two hands. In some parts of the world, though, men thought that if counting on their fingers was efficient, counting on both fingers and toes would be even better. So they developed the vigesimal system, with the number 20 as its base. Even today this system can still be found among some Eskimo, American Indian, and African tribes. It was also the mathematical basis for the great Aztec and Mayan civilizations of Mexico and Central America. Not all systems have had this simple origin; the Babylonian system, for example, had a base of 60, which could have no apparent physiological

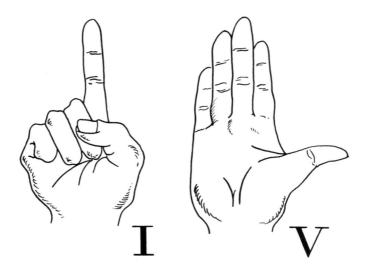

Possible relation between Roman numerals and fingers.

basis. Although some systems may have speed or ease of calculation to recommend them, none is inherently "better" than the rest, or more natural.

Another way of looking at our hands in order to use them in counting is to think of the whole hand as a unit. In this way, the system would have a base of 2. This is called the *binary system,* and is the language of electronic computers. The binary system is still very much used by people too, and it is easy to see how "natural" such a system is: we have two hands, two eyes, two feet, two ears. Some Australian aborigines—the Kulin Kurrai of the southeast and the Narrinyeri of the south—and the tribes on both sides of the Torres Strait, which separates Australia and New Guinea, count in this way, as do the Bushmen of Africa and some of the oldest tribes of South America. Leibniz, as has been said earlier, was struck by the elegance of the binary system, and was the first modern mathematician to concern himself with it.

There is an excellent reason why a computer uses the binary system and not any other, although in some ways it might be simpler if we and the computer did our mathematics in the same way. The electronic computer uses electricity, and one important fact about an electrical current is that it can be shut off and turned on again. In effect, the most widely used type of computer—the *digital computer*—has two hands but no fingers, so the most logical and economical system is the binary one: on or off, 1 or 0, yes or no. The nervous system, too, operates with an on-off electrical pulse signal, transmitting its messages in a kind of binary code.

Our decimal system is *positional*; that is, the relative position of the digits (1, 2, 3, 4, 5, 6, 7, 8, 9, and also 0) is significant. Now any number of 0's can be written down in a row; each one can be considered as representing a place, or column. If six are put down,

o o o o o o

the number shown is 0, and would be no matter how many 0's were in the row of figures. If a 2 is put in the first column at the right,

o o o o o 2

the number represented is 2, of course. But move the 2 to the second place,

o o o o 2 o

and the number becomes 20, which is 2 × 10. In other words, every time a number is moved one place to the left it is multiplied by 10.

o o o 2 o o

is 2 × 10 × 10. The binary system works in the same way, but its base is 2 instead of 10. Below are the numbers from 1 through 9 in the decimal system and their equivalents in the binary system.

Decimal	Binary
1	1
2	10
3	11
4	100
5	101
6	110
7	111
8	1000
9	1001

By looking closely at the table above, it can be seen that, just as in the decimal system, when moving a number one place to the left multiplied that number by 10, the moving of a binary digit (and remember there are only two: 1 and o) one place to the left multiplies the number by 2. So, the binary number 11 means

$$(1 \times 1) + (1 \times 2)$$
$$1 \qquad + \quad 2 \qquad = 3$$

in the decimal system. Another thing that becomes clear when one looks at the two sets of numerals is that a place or column must be completely "filled" before the addition of another number causes the movement one or more places to the left. Thus, the next addition of 1 to the decimal column will be $9 + 1 = 10$. That is, the column will be "full," and the next place is needed. If 2 is added to 7, the sum is 9, still in the first column; but, if 2 is added to 9, the sum is 11.

$$9 + 1 = 10$$
$$9 + 2 = 11$$
$$9 + 3 = 12$$

If one continues to add 1 each time, then, the right-hand column will have to be filled in order to register each progression of one digit in the second column, and so on:

$$29 + 1 = \quad 30$$
$$30 + 1 = \quad 31$$
$$31 + 1 = \quad 32$$
$$\cdots$$
$$98 + 1 = \quad 99$$
$$99 + 1 = 100$$

The same progression is true of the binary system, except that the digits in each column are limited to 1 and 0.

The binary digit is called, in the language of electronic–computer science, a *bit*. And, frequently, in speaking of the human brain, a scientist talks of the "bits" of information it holds, the number of pieces of information that it stores as yes-no, 1-0, on-off binary digits. The table of decimal and binary digits showed that it takes four places in the binary system to express all the decimal system digits. Since the people who use computers are accustomed to calculating in the decimal system, they frequently program the machines in what is called the binary-coded decimal. Suppose a programmer wants to feed the number 714 of the decimal system into the computer. He could either work it out to all the places in the binary system that such a large number would require, or he could take each digit in the number separately.

Decimal	Binary
7	0111
1	0001
4	0100

Here a four-place table has been used; and in the same way that 0 0 0 0 0 1 still equals 1, so 0 1 0 0 still equals 1 0 0 in the binary system. The programmer then feeds the number 714 into the computer as the sequence 0111, 0001, and 0100. He could put + signs or commas between all the bits representing one decimal number and a — sign to show the completion of that number. On first appearance this might seem very cumbersome and time-consuming, but since the modern electronic computer is able to process millions of bits a second this does not offer too great a practical inconvenience.

In most information-communication systems, the information is transmitted by signals of some sort, such as the dots and dashes of the Morse Code; but the silences between the dots and dashes do not communicate anything; they are wasted. However, since the two numbers of the binary system can be considered equal to the "on" (1) and "off" (0) signals of electric current, no flow of current conveys just as much information as a flow: both supply one of the two binary digits. If one wanted to, one could also refer to the two possibilities as "yes" and "no." And this opens a whole new area of computer uses, since it would then be possible for the computer, given proper instructions, to say "yes" or "no" in answer to a question. Then, assuming that a logic or system of reasoning was based on this concept, it would be possible for a computer to reason. Such a system does exist.

It is not as hard to reduce the complexities of human thought to yes-or-no quantities as one might think. The English mathematician and logician George Boole (1815–1864) developed a kind of *mathematical logic* that has proved to be ideal for computer use. In 1854 he published his great work, *An Investigation of the Laws of Thought*, which described this logic.

First, it was Boole's idea that many statements are of the same kind although they refer to very different particular things. He felt that statements could be reduced to quantities, like the *x*'s and *y*'s used in algebra to represent unknown quantities. Let us take two very different statements:

    1. If the temperature of water rises above 212 degrees Fahrenheit, then water will begin to boil.
    2. If I have enough money at the end of the week, then I will go to a movie.

Now in the first statement, let x equal "the temperature of water rises above 212 degrees Fahrenheit," and let y equal "the water will begin to boil." We get a new statement, "If x, then y."

Taking the second statement and making a similar substitution, we let x equal "I have enough money at the end of the week," and y equals "I will go to a movie." The statement then becomes "If x, then y." So the statements both have become:

    1. If x, then y.
    2. If x, then y.

This means that, although they are talking about two very different things, the same logical inference may be drawn from each of them: if x is true, then y will be true. Boole showed that, no matter what the content of a statement is, if it is in the form of "if x, then y," the same logical inference is made by it as by any and all other statements of the same type. Boole also showed that these quantities to which the statements are reduced can be manipulated mathematically, in the same way as algebraic x's and y's can be handled.

Incidentally, when looking at statements in this general

way it is important to keep them within their limits. Take, for example, the positive and negative for statement 2:

> 2a. If I have enough money at the end of the week, then I will go to a movie.

We have to assume that this statement is logically true, because it has been made. That is, for the purposes of logic, whether the person who made that statement is telling a lie or not does not matter, but

> 2b. If I do not have enough money at the end of the week, then I will not go to a movie

while it may be true practically is not necessarily logically true. This becomes obvious when other possibilities are considered. Although I may have no money left at the end of the week, I may still go to the movies because my father may give me the money, my brother may treat me, or—if I am a girl—I may have a date on Saturday night and be taken to the movies. Let us put this into a kind of mathematical shorthand. Let $-x$ be the negative or opposite of x: "I do not have enough money at the end of the week," and let $-y$ be: "I will not go to a movie." We already have the statement:

If x, then y.

Suppose $-x$ is the case. Logically we cannot say:

If x, then y.

$-x$, so $-y$.

Thus it is possible to handle a statement as a mathematical quantity, but—as in mathematics—there are rules for its manipulation. And it must be remembered that when the logician talks about true and false he is talking about statements that are logically true and false. Mathematical logic may use statements that are complete nonsense or statements that have been made by liars. "If Napoleon becomes President of the United States, then I will be a millionaire" is nonsense. But it is still an "if *x*, then *y*" type of statement. The logician can only take it and other statements, analyze them logically, and draw conclusions that are logically sound. He cannot as a logician distinguish in any philosophical or moral way between true and false, good and bad.

Essentially, then, mathematical logic is a kind of binary logic, because it is based on the premise that statements are logically either true or false, yes or no, 1 or 0. And a computer, if it is properly programmed, is an expert at mathematical logic. If a programmer wanted to put the information in the statement "If I have enough money at the end of the week, then I will go to a movie" into a computer, he could look at the shorthand we used above (if *x*, then *y*) and use the binary system instead. He could say that *x* would be programmed, with 10 arbitrarily chosen to represent *x*, as 10 — 1; — *x* could then be programmed as 10 — 0. The computer could then take this statement, along with a number of others, and perform the mathematical operations of a special kind of algebra called Boolian algebra.

As a matter of fact, about fifteen years after Boole published his work, an English economist and logician, William Stanley Jevons (1835–1882), built and exhibited a logical·machine that operated according to principles Boole had set down.

In 1938, the American mathematician Claude Shannon, then of MIT (Massachusetts Institute of Technology), published an article, "A Symbolic Analysis of Relay and Switching Circuits," in the *Transactions of the American Institute of Electrical Engineers*. This very vital technical paper related Boolian algebra to electrical circuits and the programing of computers. Only a few years later, in the midst of World War II, the preceding work was synthesized, and the first electronic digital computer was put into operation. It was based on the designs of two engineers teaching at the University of Pennsylvania, John W. Mauchly and J. P. Eckert, Jr., and was named the Electronic Numerical Integrator and Computer, ENIAC. The Second Industrial Revolution was really on its way.

5

Input, Feedback, and Output: How the Computer Works

A COMPUTER OPERATION is composed of five essential parts, and the simplified diagram on page 44 shows them in their relation to one another. They are input, arithmetic (or logic), memory (or storage), control, and output.

The input is the beginning of the computer's operation. This is the way the machine is given the information it will need in order to solve the problem the operator wants solved. The problem itself is also fed to the machine through the input, as well as any facts or numbers that should be stored in the memory until they are used. The coded information that goes into the input is called the *program,* and the person who prepares the instructions for the machine and who codes the information into computer language is the *programmer.*

Once the machine has been programmed, the *control* unit takes over. It determines what bits should be taken out of the memory unit and when, what operation should come next, and the whole progression of steps up to the solution. And, of course, the control does all this in accordance with the program. The *memory* is just that: a place to store information until it is used. The *arithmetic* unit performs all the mathematical operations that have to be done. (This is also called the logic unit, because it can manipulate statements logically in accordance with Boolean algebra.) The arithmetic unit follows the orders of the memory, and is dependent on the information stored in the memory. Finally, the computer has reached a solution to the problem, and is ready to give an answer or to take some kind of action; this is called the *output*.

Since the programmer can neither talk to the computer nor write down his instructions in a note, he must communicate with the machine in its own language, that is, in a set of symbols it will be able to use. One of the earliest devices for this purpose was the punched card used in Jacquard's loom. This method is still employed today. The cards in the loom were "read" by the needles either moving through the perforations or being held up where no perforations existed. The computer has many ways of reading the card and transferring information into the control, arithmetic, and memory units. Among them are star wheels, whose teeth can pass through the punched holes in the cards, and brushes that move over the cards' surface, transmitting in electrical impulses the information the punched or unpunched areas give.

If a whole series of punched cards could be strung together in a row and attached to one another so that they

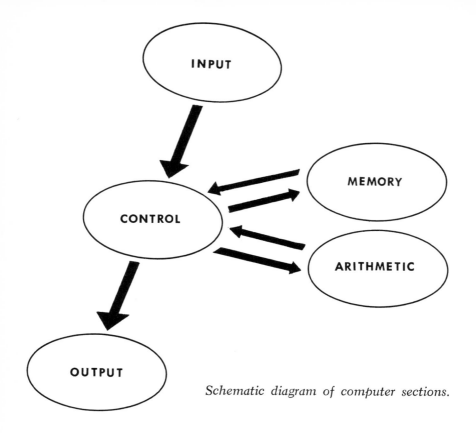

Schematic diagram of computer sections.

could be fed on one continuous roll into the machine, the operation would be faster and more efficient. This is the way that punched paper tape works. A player piano uses this kind of input. As the piano is pumped or run by electricity, the drum containing holes punched in a roll of paper revolves, the mechanism converts this code to musical sounds, and out comes "The Old Piano-roll Blues" or any other tune the roll is programmed for.

Instead of using punched paper tape, a newer and more popular way of transmitting coding information to the computer is on *magnetic tape*. This is the kind that is used in tape recorders, and is the most efficient process mentioned so far. Magnetic tape is not punched. Instead, the tape contains small areas or "spots" that can be magnetized in two opposite directions, similar to the two poles of a magnet. One direction is used for 1, the other for 0. Because the tape is coded in this way (through magnetization) it can be erased, corrected, and used over and over again. This is much cheaper than the other two procedures, since punched cards or paper tape can be given only one set of instructions: holes, once made, cannot be filled in again. Another advantage of magnetic tape is that it can pack more bits of information into the same amount of space than the other two methods. As computers' instructions become more and more complicated, this becomes a very important improvement.

Much research is being devoted to even simpler and easier ways of supplying information to the machine, without having to go through an initial coding process. Already computers have been built that can read the magnetic-ink numbers on bank checks. With computers learning to recognize numbers and letters, and sounds as well, new areas of possibilities open up. Although this sort of learning by electronic calculators is very limited today, it is possible that at some time the programmer may be able to talk to his computer, giving it all the necessary information, or even to hold a conversation with it.

Other computer operations can be performed in a number of ways. In the arithmetic operation, for example, in a desk-top adding machine each place consists of a ten-toothed gear, each tooth representing one of the digits 1 through o. When the unit gear has made a complete revolution, the 10 gear moves up one notch, and so on. In other words, as mentioned earlier, the counting is accomplished by changes of position.

A computer could use this kind of system, but a more effective way is to have an arrangement of switches, like those that turn electric lights on and off. In a calculator, a vacuum tube can serve as a kind of on-off switch.

The vacuum tube consists of an enclosure—often a glass bulb—from which much of the air has been pumped, creating a partial vacuum. Within the bulb, depending on its

The Ramac 1410, one of IBM's computer systems. The programmer is sitting at the paper-tape punch unit. The girl is standing in front of the magnetic character reader used in banking. (Courtesy International Business Machines Corporation)

type, are a number of elements. The simplest type of vacuum tube, the *diode*, was developed in the early years of
this century by the English electrical engineer Sir John
Ambrose Fleming (1849–1945). In the diode are a *cathode*
(a source of the negatively charged particles, the electrons)
and an *anode*, which is a positively charged metallic element. The electrons flow toward the anode from the cathode as long as it is positively charged. But, if the anode's
positive charge is stopped, the electrical current cannot
then travel at all.

In 1906 the American inventor Lee De Forest (b. 1873)
developed another kind of vacuum tube, the *triode*. It contains a cathode and an anode and an additional part as
well. This third element, called the *grid*, is placed between
the positively and negatively charged parts. The grid can
be given a negative charge, so that it will repel the electrons
to flow through it to the positively charged anode. The
greater the negative charge given to the grid, the more
electrons it will be able to repel. So, by controlling the
grid's negative charge, it is possible to control the strength
of the electrical current that is finally transmitted.

The ability of the vacuum tube either to transmit or
not to transmit electrical current has a familar sound to
it. It reminds one of the on-off, yes-no, 1-0 nature of the
binary system, and the way the nerve cell fires or does not
fire, or the way in which the computer operates. Vacuum
tubes are used in electronic calculators in groups called
flip-flops.

A flip-flop is made up of two vacuum tubes connected

together so that the first one is turned on (transmits current) when the first electrical pulse is transmitted. This is equivalent to a light switch being flipped on. Then, on the second pulse, the first tube goes off, but the second tube goes on. In the diagram is a series of four flip-flops. The top shows the first flip-flop on (equal to 1 in binary and decimal systems). Then a second pulse comes through, and the second flip-flop goes on, while the first one is switched off (10 in binary, 2 in decimal). Finally, in the bottom line, a third pulse of electricity switches on the first flip-flop while the second one stays on (11 in binary, 3 in decimal).

Four flip-flops in action: (top) binary number 1, (center) binary number 10, (bottom) binary number 11.

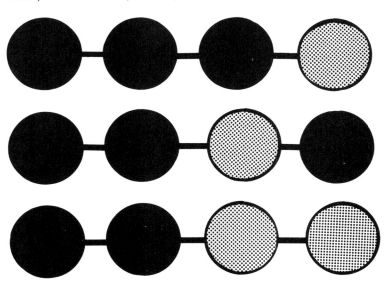

Electronic engineers are very concerned to make the flip-flops (or other ways by which the electronic calculator does arithmetic or stores its information) as small as possible. This is primarily because it would then be possible to put more flip-flops in a smaller amount of space, enabling a computer to retain and calculate with more bits. One new advance in this area is the use of transistors—consisting of tiny slabs of certain solid materials called semiconductors—which operate in a way similar to vacuum tubes but are much smaller.

The computer's calculations are performed in the arithmetic or logic unit, which can make use of the yes–no aspect of symbolic logic and Boolian algebra. (The Appendix discusses one area of computer logic—truth tables—in detail.)

It is possible for a computer to analyze a series of statements according to the rules of logic to see whether or not the conclusion arrived at is logically correct, or if one statement in the group contradicts another. In that way contracts can be studied for consistency and sense; treaties can be examined for logical content; missile instructions can be evaluated. In a time when documents are becoming more numerous and more complicated, man is going to need all the help he can get from his computer partners.

The information needed by the computer is stored in the memory or storage unit. Punched cards that can be filed and stored make up one kind of computer memory. Another device that was used a great deal in the early days of computers was the vacuum tube flip-flop, which, as long as it was on or off in a series, retained its particular bit of information. And of course magnetic tape can be used not only for input but also as a memory unit.

One improvement on magnetic tape is the magnetic drum, a cylinder on which several tracks of tape can be wound. This again increases the number of bits of information that can be stored. The drum can be supplemented by indexed "libraries" of magnetic tape, which are stored outside the computer but to which it can refer if necessary. But, although tape cuts down on storage area and increases the number of bits that can be stored, it is—by computer standards—very time-consuming. When information is recorded on tape it is in a certain order. Suppose the computer had a series of ten bits of information recorded on a tape. If it had to refer first to the third bit, then to the seventh, then to the second, and finally to the ninth, in a certain order, the memory tape would have to be rolled back and forth as the bits were found. This is, of course, inefficient.

One of the most widely used memory systems employs a device by which a bit of information can be located at once. This is the *magnetic core*. Each core is a small, doughnut-shaped piece of ferrite material that can be magnetized in either one of two directions, again, like one of the two poles of a magnet. Each core is strung on wires, and the series of wires is placed on a frame. Every magnetic core is at the intersection of two wires, one vertical and the other horizontal, and the machine is able to get at any one piece of information as quickly as at any other. In this way, bits can be located with greater speed by the machine, each core being capable of storing one bit.

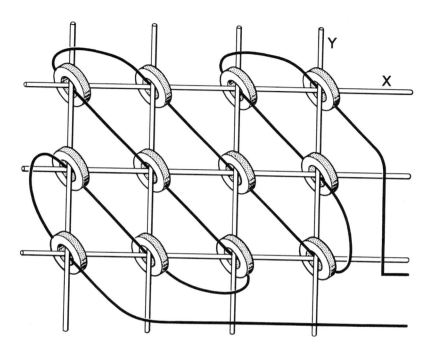

Magnetic ferrite memory cores strung on a matrix of wires. The
x *number and* y *number of each core can be used to locate the*
bit of information it is storing. (Courtesy Bell Telephone
Laboratories)

The memory unit is one of the most important aspects
of the electronic calculator; and engineers know that the
more bits it can store, the more complex the computer's
calculations can be. Because of this, a great deal of effort
is being devoted to miniaturization. It is possible to take
strips of film and divide them into very small areas. Then

the coating of emulsion on the film can be either exposed to light or screened from it in each of these tiny areas, creating dark and light spots equivalent to the on-off of flip-flops, or of any of the other yes-or-no ways of bit storage.

A very similar kind of memory unit is used in some new computers. It consists of a piece of glass that has been coated with tiny dots of magnetized metal, and it can be coded like the other types of storage. Each dot can record one bit.

It is interesting to note that many scientists feel that, as we learn more about how tiny, complex, organic molecules are constructed, we will be able to apply this knowledge to electronic miniaturization in order to make more complex, more effective computers.

Every complex operation needs a command post. The computer, like the brain, must have a control unit. To the control unit comes the program for the whole operation that the computer is undertaking. But, unlike a human controller, the electronic control unit cannot improvise action and respond to unexpected situations or emergencies. It cannot supply information on its own in order to complete a program that has not been sufficient. At this time, a computer is only as good, efficient, and correct as its program.

If a computer is programmed that $2 + 2 = 4$, all is well and good. But, if the finger of the programmer slips, and the instructions reach the machine as $2 + 2 = 5$, there will be trouble. Because of the possibility of errors, programs usually include some way of checking for inconsistencies and contradictions. Then, the computer can signal that

Another type of computer memory component, the electronic ferrite core memory unit. (Courtesy Bell Telephone Laboratories)

it cannot proceed because it does not have enough information or because its results were checked and found inconsistent.

The control unit uses the information in the program to start and stop the calculation and to give specific orders as the work progresses, such as: add, store this until needed, bring such-and-such a bit out of the memory unit, divide, and so on. Since these machines operate so quickly, it is essential that a bit of information or a pulse of electricity be in the right place at the right time. The control unit is the timekeeper of the whole procedure.

The last stage of any operation is the result, or output. The output is in a way the reverse of the input, and its information comes out of the computer in any of the ways originally programmed. The answer can be fed to a machine that will punch cards with the correct information on them, or it can be put on magnetic tape, and so on. But, just as the computer does not understand our language very well, the binary language is hard for us to read and interpret. High-speed printing devices are therefore used to take the output and convert it into decimal-system digits or letters of the alphabet. But there are other kinds of output.

A computer programmed to write and play music would produce output in the form of musical notes. A computer

RIGHT: A *thimbleful of memory cores, each one* 21/1000 *of an inch in diameter.* (*Courtesy International Business Machines Corporation*) FAR RIGHT: *Another type of memory unit, a "Microstack" using printed circuits.* (*Courtesy Indiana General*)

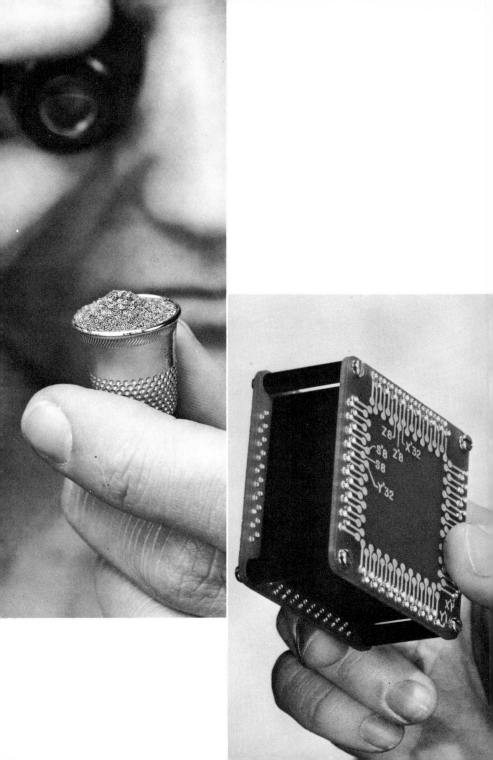

could even "speak." It could have access to a whole series of recorded words attached to a speaker system. Every bit of the output would then be translated into the correct word, and the machine would recite its answer.

When electronic computers or calculators are spoken of in this book, the *digital computer* is usually meant. But, actually, it is only one kind of computer. The digital computer deals with digits, numbers, or discrete mathematical units—with how many of something there are. The number 1 and the number 2 are separate from one another, discrete. An abacus or an adding machine is an example of a digital calculator.

But there are other measuring devices that tell "how much" (how fast you are traveling) rather than "how many" (how many miles you have traveled). These are called analog calculators. Their name comes from the words "analogous" or "analogue," meaning something that is comparable to something else. One such device is the speedometer. When a driver looks at his speedometer to find how fast he is driving, he does not see a face on which numbers appear for 40 miles per hour, then 41, then 42. Instead, there is an indicator that moves gradually and continuously along the face of the instrument.

Analog measuring devices are much faster than digital ones for the most part, but are less accurate. So analog computers are used where numerical precision and accuracy is not central.

The Systron-Donner 3200 analog computer. (Courtesy Systron-Donner Corporation)

What good is an analog computer, then? It deals with the problem as a whole rather than with the separate parts, so, it can be used as a model of the way a whole system behaves. For example, the photograph shows a table-top analog computer, the Systron-Donner 3200 made by the Systron-Donner Corporation, New York. It can be used, among other things, in biomedical research. For this computer can be programmed to simulate (or imitate) certain physiological reactions and can be used in research, such as finding the mechanical properties of arteries or the way nerves and muscles interact. Although its increasingly sophisticated brother, the digital computer, tends to become more and more important, the analog machine still fulfills a vital function. It is interesting, too, that the first really successful large-scale computer was the analog-type Differential Analyzer built by the American scientist Vannevar Bush in 1927.

If in some ways the electronic computer operates like the brain, it should also be possible to construct electronic mechanisms that imitate some aspects of animal and human behavior, such as unpredictable response, conditional response, learning, and game playing. The next two chapters deal with these areas of cybernetics.

6

Bionics: Mouse, Tortoise, Hand, and Others

SOME OF the most interesting and amusing scientific reports of the last few years have been written about a certain kind of creature, which includes a mouse learning to run a maze and two tortoises named Elmer and Elsie. The very remarkable thing about these creatures is that they are not animals; they are electrically powered simulators of certain aspects of animal behavior.

These devices and many others fall within a new scientific discipline named *bionics*. The word comes from the Greek *bion*, meaning unit of life. Bionics, a subdivision of cybernetics, is the study of the similarities and relationships between the machine and the brain and of imitations of life—the construction of machines based on biological knowledge. This new science was named at a conference held by the United States Air Force in 1960 to discuss its possibilities.

An interesting aspect of animal self-regulation was studied by the American physiologist Walter B. Cannon. In 1932 he published the first detailed study of this behavior and gave it the name *homeostasis*, from two Greek roots: *homoios*, meaning "like" or "similar to," and *stasis*, "a standing still." The homeostatic mechanism of organisms works to maintain the equilibrium of the internal environment of the body, the right chemical balance, temperature, water content, and so forth. The great French physiologist Claude Bernard (1813–1878) was the man who first described this characteristic. Homeostasis, then, is the tendency of the organism to react against disruptive body changes by producing an equal and opposite change in order to keep the body at a state of equilibrium. Again—like the thermostat constantly regulating room temperature, or the hypothalamus controlling body temperature—all the homeostatic mechanisms of the animal body work to keep it in its optimal state.

Suppose we consider any living system—like the homeostatic mechanisms—that is self-regulating and receives, evaluates, and acts on information communicated to it. Now, if a scientist wished to create a mechanical system that simulated the living system, he could proceed in one of two ways.

One procedure would be to study all the components of the living system. By finding out exactly how a neuron is constructed, how electrical pulses are transmitted, how memories are stored in the brain, and so on, the scientist could build a model out of manufactured parts that worked in exactly the same way as the organic parts of the system.

Out of plastics, liquids, and metallic wires, he might construct something that looked just like and functioned just like an animal nervous system. He could do this, that is, if he knew enough about each separate component, if he could afford to build the model, and if he were as interested in the parts as in the system as a whole.

The second way to approach the problem would use what engineers call the *black box* concept. This means that the scientist considers the system he is studying as a black box, a mystery, with unknown parts on the inside that respond in a certain way when particular information (in the case of electrical engineering the response of the apparatus to an electrical current) is fed into it. In this method what becomes central is not the parts (the wires, screws, batteries, and so on) that make the black box run, but the way it responds (how it acts). Similarly, a scientist could study a living organism and see the way it responds to certain information that is fed into it—study the input and output. He could then proceed to construct a mechanical system that, upon being fed the same or similar information, responded like the organism. Whether the machine used vacuum tubes or transistors or anything else instead of neurons, muscles, and other living tissue would not matter.

When a scientist builds a device that simulates a living system, he uses the black box concept. One machine built along these lines by the English scientist W. Ross Ashby is called Homeostat and was constructed to imitate the biological phenomena described by Dr. Cannon.

Made up of a series of groups of components that are freely supplied with energy, Homeostat is constructed so

W. Ross Ashby's Homeostat. (*Courtesy Philippe Constantin*)

that when any attempted changes are imposed from the outside—in this case, the changes would cause movement of indicators (needles on a dial) connected to the components—the various parts of the mechanism interact with one another in a very complex feedback pattern. This pattern continues until the change is negated or neutralized and the needles return to the point indicating stability. The change is never predictable. Sometimes the current going into the mechanism is varied in accordance with a table of random numbers, sometimes the various sections of the interacting mechanism are unplugged or re-plugged in another way. None of this has any lasting effect on Homeostat, which continues to make adjustments until it again finds its own equilibrium.

Machines built to look like and imitate certain animals are not unusual. From the time of Archytas of Tarentum (c. 428–347 B.C.), the Greek philosopher and scientist who was said to have constructed a wooden pigeon that actually flew, men have built automatons that performed some animal-like actions.

In 1929, Henri Piraux, chief of technical publicity of the Société Française Philips, demonstrated Philodog at the International Radio Exhibition in Paris. A rather charming toy, Philodog was sensitive to light, and followed a flashlight that was turned on toward it around in a circle. If the light came too close, Philodog barked in resentment. But Philodog had no originality; it only did what it had been told to do, performing a few predictable actions, like the mechanical birds that move their wings and twitter a few tunes.

But in the 1950's other light-sensitive mechanical animals were built on a completely different basis. The English neurologist and electroencephalographer Grey Walter built several electrically powered tortoises. These machines were given the "mock-biological" name of *Machina speculatrix*, and the Adam and Eve of this strange line of "creatures" were Elmer and Elsie. They got their names from *Electro Mechanical Robots, Light-Sensitive, with Internal and External stability.*

Elmer and Elsie were small, mobile, smooth-shelled mechanisms with one eye (*photoelectric cell*) used to search for light stimuli. Extremely simple machines, the tortoises were built with two small vacuum tubes, two sense organs (light and touch), and two motors (one for crawling along the ground and one for steering).

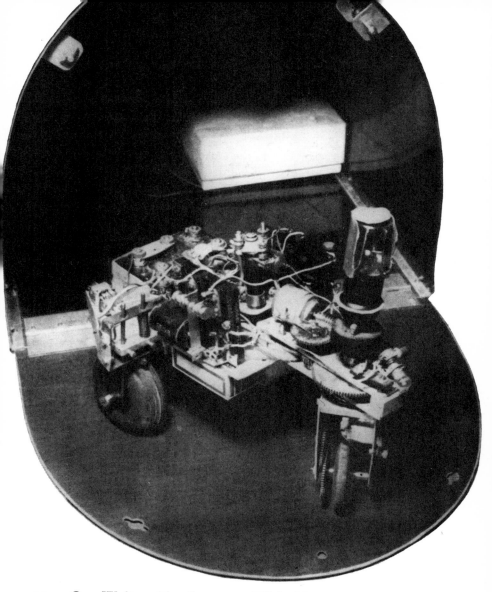

LEFT: *Grey Walter with wife, son, and Elsie.* (*Courtesy Philippe Constantin*) ABOVE: *The "anatomy" of Elsie.* (*Courtesy of Philippe Constantin*)

Elmer and Elsie were powered by batteries that could be recharged. The tortoises could come home to their nests to "feed" by plugging into a power source located near a strong light. So, when they were "hungry" the tortoises were attracted by strong light. But, once fed, they sought soft lights until their batteries were run down and they had to hunt for food again.

When there was not sufficient light, Elmer or Elsie crawled along the ground searching for a strong enough source. If they came to an obstacle, they would backtrack, try again in another direction, and keep trying until they could get around whatever lay in their path. Upon finding the right kind of light, the tortoises steered toward it. That is, they were *phototropic* in a way. The biological phenomenon of phototropism occurs when plants or animals are attracted to light. If the light was too strong for the tortoise it would retreat. And, if there was more than one light source available, Elmer and Elsie would visit first one, then another, until all had been examined.

The tortoises are more than amusing playthings. By their unpredictable behavior they have acted in ways reminiscent of animals, and Dr. Walter has shown that only a very few electronic components are necessary to initiate this kind of behavior.

Elsie's "offspring," Cora (Conditioned Reflex Analog), took another step forward. Cora was sensitive to light and to some sounds as well. At first Cora was shown a strong light, and reacted to it. Then a whistle was blown, making a sound Cora could receive, at the same time the light was shown. Cora associated the whistle with the light, and

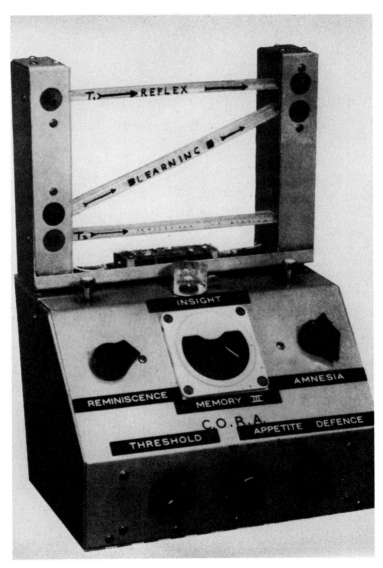

Grey Walter's Cora. (Courtesy Philippe Constantin)

after a period of time reacted to the whistle alone in the way it had reacted to the light. This is startlingly like the experiments on animal reflexes made by Ivan Pavlov that were mentioned in the third chapter.

Another more complex bionic model has been built recently. This model grew out of the work, a few years ago, of the neurophysiologist Jerome Y. Lettvin and his associates at MIT, Warren McCulloch, Humberto R. Maturana, and Walter H. Pitts. These scientists were studying the frog's eye, and they reported their results in the paper, "What the Frog's Eye Tells the Frog."

A project officer, with an electronic frog's eye, built for the Air Force to simulate electronically the function of the frog's retina. (Courtesy U.S. Air Force)

A network of artificial nerve cells being assembled at Bell Telephone Laboratories. (Courtesy Bell Telephone Laboratories)

The MIT scientists studied a small part of the retina of the frog's eye and the signals that were sent by the nerve fibers to the brain. Variously shaped objects were passed before the frog's eye so that its response to them could be measured. A very remarkable thing was noticed. If the flat edge of a rectangular object was thrust before the eye, no signal was sent to the brain at all. The frog did not see the object. But if this same rectangular object was passed with a corner coming first, rather than a straight edge, the eye responded and sent signals to the brain. After experimenting with disks of various sizes, the men found that the frog did not respond to angled or circular objects that were too small or too large. But, when a disk, perceived by the frog as if it were a fly at about catching distance, appeared, the nerve cells sent strong signals out. In other words, the frog's eye has a built-in "bug-detector" that tells it when possible food is near. Lettvin and his associates found that what the frog perceives of our world is very limited. It does not see—or at least does not concern itself with—objects that are not of a certain shape or size. The remainder of the world just does not exist for the frog; that is, no signals telling of it are sent out by the optic nerve cells. One wonders if humans have similar optical limitations.

By using groups of artificial neurons and photoelectric cells, scientists have created a bionic mechanism that responds in the same way. Just as the basic element of the nervous system is the neuron, the basic part of a bionic computer is the artificial neuron, an electric circuit of a special type.

There are various kinds of artificial neuron. One, Artron, built by the Melpar Corporation of Falls Church, Virginia, is a component of a very interesting bionic computer that operates a mouse who can learn to run a maze. This miraculous mouse is now being studied by the Air Force at their Wright-Patterson Air Force Base near Dayton, Ohio. The mouse begins its first time through the maze with no special instructions or tendencies to follow one part of the maze more than another. It finds its way through by a process of trial and error, bumping into blind alleys, retracing its path, and beginning over and over again.

Each time the mouse begins the maze again it has learned something about how the paths are laid out, and gets through in less time. Finally, it can make its way through the maze with no errors in a matter of seconds. This device is only one of a series of maze-running machines that have been constructed.

One interesting refinement that is being worked on now will teach the mouse to associate colors with right and wrong turns. Green will indicate a right turn, red a wrong one. After the mouse "learns" what the colors mean, it could be put into any maze and, if the turnings are marked, run through it quickly and without error the first time.

The practical applications of such a machine are numerous. It is possible that a bionic control system may

The electronic mouse at Wright-Patterson Air Force Base beginning to run its maze. (Courtesy U.S. Air Force)

Perceptron being shown the letter "C." (Courtesy Cornell Aeronautics Laboratory)

eventually be able to pilot planes and function in any way where it can be guided by signposts such as colored lights.

Another bionic system that would interest the armed forces would be a complex pattern-recognition system. Going far beyond the capabilities of radar, the widely used electronic object-detecting device, such a system could, when launched in a satellite, report on significant happenings on the earth. This device would be able to know the difference between the path of a missile and simple deviations from cloud patterns. It could distinguish between friendly and alien aircraft or weapons, and even report on large military movements.

One forerunner of this kind of system may be a machine constructed by Dr. Frank Rosenblatt and his associates at Cornell University. Perceptron, as the machine is called, is learning how to perceive and recognize letters of the alphabet when they are placed in front of its photocell "eyes."

Sceptron (Spectral Comparative Pattern Recognizer), built by the Sperry Gyroscope Company of New York, recognizes spoken information. For example, it can be taught to recognize the word "five" and to react so that every time the word "five" is spoken Sceptron will light the numeral five on its response panel. So sensitive are

The word "five" has just been spoken into a microphone, thereby triggering a Sceptron to react by displaying the number "5." (Courtesy Sperry-Gyroscope Company)

Sceptrons that they have refused to respond to the voice of their instructor when he is emotionally upset. The components of a Sceptron are not expensive, costing about $2.50, and a similar but more complex model could take oral dictation and type out letters or memos as they were read to it.

The last bionic computer to be discussed here is Hand. It was developed at MIT by the Swiss scientist Dr. Heinrich Ernst. Hand is a mechanical hand controlled by a computer. It has a pair of tongs for fingers, and is covered with a plastic "skin" containing photocells that respond to light and other electrical cells responsive to touch. Hand can be instructed to locate an object, pick it up, and put it in a particular place.

Sceptron, Hand, Elmer and Elsie, and other devices discussed in this chapter are all self-regulating systems. Like animals or humans they operate on a simple set of general instructions, learning themselves, as they proceed, from their experience. It now takes a programmer several months to prepare instructions for a computer that then runs through them and comes up with an answer usually in a matter of minutes. Under many circumstances the time, energy, and money saved by a bionic computer is great, and its great flexibility is an advantage, too. Of course, since the bionic devices have to learn, like us they would not be ready to function fully as soon as they were "born." They would have to "go to school" in order to learn their jobs.

Perhaps an even more important aspect of bionics is the insight into human behavior and the structure of the

A demonstration Sceptron with its "mask" being changed. The mask contains the Sceptron's vocabulary program. (Courtesy Sperry Gyroscope Company)

body that scientists are gaining by its means. Once a system of artificial neurons has been created to function like a part of the nervous system, biologists, neurologists, physiologists, engineers, and physicists can go on to other experiments. By trying things out on the artificial neuron—things that cannot be experimentally tested on the living organism—man will gain more knowledge of what he is and how he functions.

One of the early anticipators of bionics was the great French philosopher René Descartes (1596–1650). In 1637 he published his *Discourse on Method,* and in Part V offers a prophetic section. Discussing the nervous system and the senses, and the bodily response to the objects that are presented to the senses, Descartes says:

This will hardly seem strange to those who know how many motions can be produced in automata or machines which can be made by human industry, although these automata employ very few wheels and other parts in comparison with the large number of bones, muscles, nerves, arteries, veins, and all the other component parts of each animal.

(This is one of the points Dr. Walter made with his tortoises.)

René Descartes (1596–1650). (The Bettmann Archive)

Descartes goes on:

Here (in an unpublished work) I paused to show that if there were any machines which had the organs and appearance of a monkey or of some other unreasoning animal, we would have no way of telling that it was not of the same nature as these animals. But if there were a machine which had such a resemblance to our bodies and imitated our actions as far as is morally possible, there would always be two absolutely certain methods of recognizing that it was still not truly a man. The first is that it could never use words or other signs for the purpose of communicating its thoughts to others, as we do. It is indeed conceivable that a machine could be so made that it would utter words . . . . But it could never modify its phrases to reply to the sense of whatever was said in its presence, as even the most stupid men can do. The second method of recognition is that, although such machines could do many things as well as, or perhaps even better than, men, they would infallibly fail in certain others, by which we would discover that they did not act by understanding or reason, but only by the disposition of their organs.

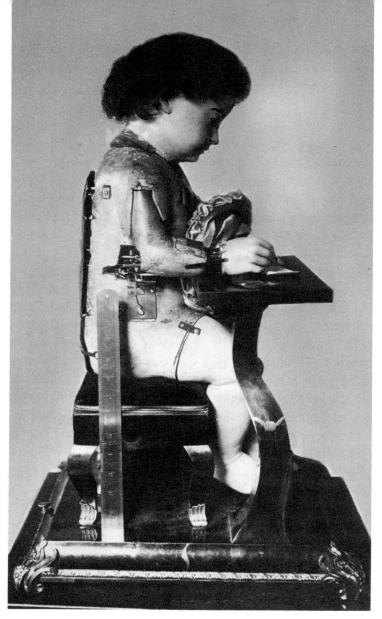

The Jacquet-Droz writing automaton. (The Bettmann Archive)

7

Artificial Intelligence and Learning: Games, Poetry, and Translation

FROM ABOUT the eighteenth century on, as machines became more complex, a great deal of energy was devoted to creating imitations of human, rather than simply animal, activity. In 1736 a French inventor, Jacques de Vaucanson (1709–1782), built a flute player, the size of a human, that could play 12 melodies on the German flute. Not only did this mechanism finger the instrument properly, it moved its lips and actually tongued the flute to control the flow of wind into it.

Then in 1757, the mechanician to the court of Francis I of Austria, Friedrich von Knaus, built the first writing machine. In the Technological Museum of Vienna this machine still functions today. An improvement on von Knaus' machine was made by a French inventor, Pierre

Jacquet-Droz (b. 1721). In 1774 Droz amazed European audiences with an automaton, about the size of a young boy, that could sit and write on a pad before it. This was followed by another writer and a very charming girl-automaton that could play the harpsichord.

But these were only mechanisms doing a few predetermined things. They were perhaps more complex and amusing than music boxes, but not much more original. Men still tried to create another kind of machine, one that could defy Descartes' distinction between automata and humans and "modify its phrases to reply to the sense of whatever was said in its presence . . . ."

And indeed, in 1769 all of Europe was awe-struck before just such a machine. The game of chess is probably the most difficult intellectual pastime Western man has, and a machine that could play even passable chess in response to unpredictable countermoves of a human opponent would indeed be defying Descartes. The "Maelzel Chess Automaton" did just this. Introduced by the Hungarian Baron Wolfgang von Kempelen (1734–1804), the chess automaton played Maria Theresa of Austria as its first opponent. Before the hushed audience of the assembled court, the machine moved on to victory.

The Maelzel chess player won most of its games as it toured the Continent and, later, the United States. Among its illustrious opponents were Frederick the Great, King of Prussia, and Napoleon. Finally, in 1854, this marvel was destroyed in a fire in Philadelphia. But no one could believe in the existence of a machine that *really* functioned in this way. The great American writer Edgar Allan Poe

The Maelzel chess player.

(1809–1849) wrote an exposé of the chess player. He and all the other doubters were right. The machine was a fraud. Not an automaton at all, it was a well-constructed piece of machinery controlled by a very good chess player hidden within. About twenty-five years after the chess-playing machine was destroyed, an English magician, John Nevil Maskelyne (1839–1917), demonstrated "Psycho." This whist-playing device was unfortunately also a fraud, controlled by an off-stage confederate using a pneumatic tube.

But the attempt to construct an authentic game-playing machine continued, and in 1914 the first one was shown. The Spanish inventor Leonardo Torres y Quevedo, Director of Laboratorio de Automática in Madrid, exhibited a machine that really did play a very simple end game of chess (that is, the last few moves of the game).

In the last few years the idea for a computer-run chess player has been developed by Claude Shannon, and a game-playing computer has learned to play checkers with its creator, Arthur Samuel of IBM. How can a machine that only knows "yes" or "no," 1 or 0, on or off, learn to play chess? The chessboard and the entire game are translated into language the computer understands and knows how to handle. First, the squares are coded. A chessboard is divided into ranks, the horizontal rows, and files, the vertical rows. So, like the magnetic memory cores discussed earlier, a chess piece can be found easily because it is always at the intersection of a rank and a file. A black knight might move from its original position of 71 (rank row 7, file row 1) to 50 or 52.

Pieces are also given numbers, from 1 for the pawn, up to 6 for the king. Black pieces are negative, white positive. So the black knight is -2. The first move would be coded -2, 71, 50. It is an easy step to translate these numbers into binary numbers.

The computer now knows where pieces are and how to instruct moves; it then must be able to reason the game out. It has been calculated that the possible number of moves in an average game of chess is something like 10^{120} (the number 1 with 120 zeros after it). Clearly, it is not feasible to instruct the machine on all possible moves and on replies to all possible countermoves by an opponent whose game will not be predictable. It would take the machine years to evaluate a situation before a piece was moved.

So, some "rules" have to be made. A chess player always values the relative worth of each piece. To exchange your pawn (the weakest piece in the game) for your opponent's queen (the most powerful piece in the game) is sensible. To give up a queen in order to take a pawn is foolhardy. Roughly, it can be figured that every piece is worth a certain number of pawns; for example a queen is worth nine pawns, a bishop three. The computer could then be instructed to evaluate its move in the light of

Norbert Wiener and G. Torres y Quevedo, son of the inventor, playing a losing game against the Torres y Quevedo machine. (Courtesy Philippe Constantin)

"pawn power." It could examine all its possible moves and see which would result in the greatest strengthening of pawn power.

This still does not make the game simple and straightforward. A good chess player look many moves ahead, perhaps as many as twenty. He looks at what he will do, figures what the opponent will probably do, adjusts his idea of his next move to what the opponent's first answer probably will be, and so on. And, each time a piece is moved, the process of evaluation and adjustment begins all over again. To look ahead two moves, examining all the possible moves and countermoves, would take 1,024 evaluations; for four moves, the machine would have to consider 1,148,576 alternatives.

Even at the high speed with which a computer operates, this would still take too much time. Some compromise has to be reached. The human player does not, and cannot, consider all the alternatives. He uses some selection when considering how to move. The computer could be programmed in the same way. It would only consider the most important of the possible combinations, and in this way it could look far enough into the future to see how each of the major possible moves would work out. This is based, it must be remembered, on how the opponent will *probably* respond. The machine has no program informing it of how the human opponent definitely will answer any move. But, as Claude Shannon has pointed out, "The chief weakness of this type of machine is that it will not learn by its mistakes. The only way to improve its play is to improve the program." Think of a computer that could

learn how to improve its own play once it had been programmed! After playing tournament after tournament
(even playing against itself) this machine could become a
champion player.

This kind of machine is not impossible. Arthur Samuel's
checker-playing computer is able to learn by consulting its
memory core, which stores information on what has hap-
pened in previous games when the same situation has
arisen. Since checkers is a much simpler game than chess,

*A chessboard showing how rank and file numbers and piece
values can be used to indicate moves numerically.*

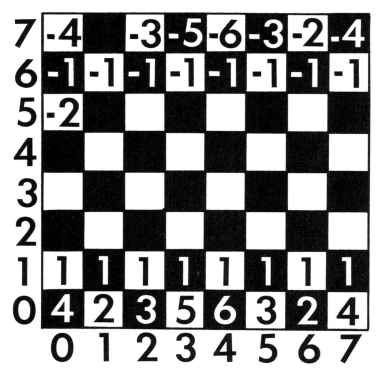

situations do repeat themselves more frequently. Of course, there is a problem of memory space. Not all the moves of all the games can be stored. Dr. Samuel has therefore programmed the machine to evaluate its memories by the standards of how long they have been stored and how frequently they are referred to. After a certain amount of time the unusual moves are discarded from the memory.

The dedicated scientists who are working on these machines are not eccentrics spending thousands of dollars on amusements that will help them to pass a rainy afternoon. What is learned from game-playing machines will be put to use in many ways. Chess can be looked upon as a kind of war between white and black, with each move a battle fought; the strategy of each side is a ruthless plan to win. In war sacrifices of men are made when it is necessary, or when an advantage will come of a move. War is perhaps the most serious "game."

Weapons of the last twenty years have changed so drastically that tactics have had to change too. How can a general know whether or not a particular kind of strategy will work, unless he has a real battle to learn from? His education would be costly, in money and in human lives. Now, there is a bloodless way to simulate battles and see what the results are. The IBM Simulation Laboratory at Owego, New York, for example, has conducted simulated battles by programming the information into the computer, which can furnish information on the numbers of dead, of wounded, and of physically fit surviving troops; on the tactical advantage that would result; and on other militarily important data.

Arthur Samuel playing checkers against a computer. (Courtesy International Business Machines Corporation)

If there should ever be another war it will probably be fought with large-scale atomic weapons capable of devastating entire cities. The government has used computers simulating the conditions of nuclear battles with various strategies of attack and defense, so that it may plan the safest and most power-gaining war strategy. So, the computer evaluates numbers representing not only pawns and queens, but also men and women, civilians and soldiers, as it fights battle after battle in a theoretical, mathematically constructed war.

Let us next move from this grim world to the world of art. In May 1962, *Horizon*, a widely read magazine of the arts, published the significant works of a new poet in an article, "A New American Poet Speaks: The Works of A. B." One of A. B.'s most successful poems was "Girls":

> *All girls sob like slow snows.*
> *Near a couch, that girl won't weep.*
> *Rains are silly lovers, but I am not shy.*
> *Stumble, moan, go,*
>   *this girl might sail on the desk.*
> *No foppish, deaf, cool kisses are very humid.*
> *This girl is dumb and soft.*

Auto-Beatnik. (Courtesy Librascope Division of General Precision, Incorporated)

A. B. will probably never win the Nobel Prize, but then he doesn't know what it is. His full name was Auto-Beatnik (he is now more respectably named Auto-Poet), and he is a computer programmed by R. M. Worthy and his associates at the Librascope Division of General Precision, Inc., Glendale, California. Auto-Beatnik had a vocabulary of 3,500 words when it "wrote" the poem "Girls." It used them to write the poem in a very specifically programmed way.

There are four different groups of words in the program. The first contains singular nouns, the second transitive verbs, the third adjectives, and the fourth articles and pronouns. For example,

1	2	3	4
tree	knows	red	this
cat	runs	skinny	an
dog	throws	fat	a
table	gives	young	the
porcupine	drinks	good	every

The aim is to get the computer to write a sentence that makes grammatical sense. Words chosen from columns at random, say 4–2–1–3, would result in a sentence like "Every throws table fat." This not only makes no sense in that it has no meaning, but it makes no grammatical sense. English, like any language, has a structure. The computer can be instructed to imitate that structure by choosing its words from columns in a certain order (although within the column the choice is still random). A pattern such as

4–1–2–4–3–1–2 would result in the sentence "This cat knows a red dog," or "Every tree drinks the young table." Meaning still is only accidental, but there is a structure, something to recall the way the English language operates, its grammar and word forms.

English has different kinds of sentence structure, and Auto-Beatnik can be instructed to construct each line of its "poetry" according to a different sentence pattern. It can also rhyme the poem in any rhyme scheme. In "Girls" the lines do not logically follow one another; each one is a separate unit. But Worthy did want to simulate a kind of unification within the poem in order to make it appear more like a unit.

To do this he programmed the repetition of certain key words. The computer was programmed to choose at random a certain number of nouns before beginning the poem. Each noun was given a certain percentage value to insure that it appeared in the poem with a certain frequency. For example, in the poem quoted the word "girl" was assigned a high percentage, and appeared four times.

But poetry, indeed language, has another very important element beyond grammatical structure: it has meaning. In order to write a meaningful poem, Auto-Beatnik has to write about something. A simple program would not be adequate and would have to be replaced by a very complex one that included considerations of logic, reasoning, and semantics. But Worthy is optimistic. He says, "We believe that a computer can be programmed to write meaningful and relevant sentences in proper English. And we hope to tackle the problem of conversing with a computer in completely natural speech, as we would with a person.... Eventually a true man-machine dialogue should be possible."

One practical result of both the game-playing machines and of Auto-Beatnik may be translation from one language to another. In the sciences, law, medicine, the arts, business, and other fields, many important articles are written in numerous languages. Buried in the technical and professional journals all over the world may be important, even crucial, information for work going on in another country; the access to such information is now quite inadequate.

It might seem simple to construct a translating machine. After all, a computer could be fed an extensive English vocabulary, each word given an identifying number, and a French vocabulary with equivalent words given the same numbers (perhaps positive numbers for English words and negative ones for French). Then, if — 7 were *homme*, the machine could locate 7, which would be "man."

Language is more complex and subtle than this, however. "Girl," "young lady," "young woman," "teenager," "bobby soxer," "tomato," and "chick" all mean different things and may not have exact equivalents in another language. Moreover, "tomato" and "chick" also have other definitions, and how is the machine to know which kind of tomato is meant? D. S. Halacy, Jr., in his book, *Computers*, mentions an interesting, perhaps apocryphal, experiment. A computer, programmed with both an English and a Russian vocabulary, was fed the adage "The spirit is willing, but the flesh is weak." The machine was to translate from English into Russian and back into English. The results: "The vodka is strong, but the meat is rotten."

Languages have different grammatical structures, too. Chinese sentences are not like Spanish or German ones. And within a language spelling and punctuation may be misleading. Without evaluating an entire sentence a computer could hardly distinguish between "read" (present tense) and "read" (past tense); or, without the hyphen, between "recreate" and "re-create."

A number of research teams are at work on the problem of translation by computer. As man's scientific and technical knowledge grows, and as the world community draws closer together, this will become an increasingly important problem. Computers can help in other similar ways as well. They can index articles, periodicals, or books. With more and more printed matter flooding the market, they could abstract from long scientific treatises, dissertations, or technical papers the most significant and original aspects. They could store whole works, index them by key word, and make available the entire work or selected passages. A computer with access to a complete chemical library could, with proper programming, turn up all the pertinent material on, for example, oxidation. Machines can also be used to save countless man-hours in professions such as law, searching through patent records or court precedents in hours instead of months or years.

When man looks at the electronic computer and sees one supposedly unique human quality after another taken away from him by the machine, he may fall back on a major distinction between animal and machine and want to say, "Well, at least I can reproduce my own kind. I can father a human child." But now machines can, in a sense, reproduce their own kind. That is, they can create new "organisms" like themselves out of parts that can be obtained by them from their environment and utilized by other machines operating under instructions supplied by the "parent" device. But the animal uses food and a highly complex series of chemical transformations, while the machine uses mechanical parts, such as wires, batteries, photoelectric cells, and so on. Yet it is possible for a machine so programmed and with access to necessary materials to construct another. Moreover, simple machines can be used to design more complex ones—the Remington-Rand Corporation of New York used Univac I and Univac II in the design of Univac III, for example.

8

Information
and Communication

EVERY COMMUNICATION SYSTEM communicates information, and the better the system, the fewer errors it makes in the communication process. "Telephone" is a popular game among children. All the players line up, and the first player whispers a message to the second. The second whispers *what he has heard* to the third, and so on to the end of the chain. As anyone who has played the game knows, the beginning phrase often has little resemblance to the phrase that is repeated by the last person.

When one speaks on the telephone to a friend in a different country, or even a different city, it is usually harder to understand what he is saying than if he was in the same city. The signals—the words we speak into the telephone—are not the same when they are communicated as when they are received. They have been distorted or obliterated by *noise.* In communication theory—or information theory, as it is also called—anything that interferes with the transmission of the message is called "noise." And, of course, the amount of noise in any communication system has a relationship to the percentage of information that the system communicates. Noise can be considered as synonymous with error.

If a wife sends her husband a telegram saying, "Come home, darling, I love you and miss you," he may receive it as "Czme, dorling, I missyou." But he will probably still be able to decipher the message, even though words have been left out and letters changed. This is because English, like any language, has redundant words, which say pretty much the same thing in several different ways. In fact, Claude Shannon, the father of information theory, has calculated that the English language is 75 to 80 per cent redundant. Moreover, each spoken word contains about ten pieces of information not related to the message—information about the speaker's personality, the weather, his environment, and so on.

One way to correct error, or to combat noise, is to send a message over and over again until it has been received so many times that the entire message is completely deciphered. Every time the message is sent, less information is communicated. This is because the amount of new information that is added grows smaller and smaller as the content of the message takes shape. At the beginning, nothing is known; as the message is sent over and over again, less and less is unknown. In the mathematical theory of information, measurement is communicated by bits, the same 1–0, yes-no bits discussed earlier in this book.

In other words, this theory of communication states that the most complex message can be reduced to yes-no, on-off bits. When shown a four-sided figure, I can ask, "What is this four-sided figure?" The answer would be that it is a square, a rectangle, a parallelogram, or whatever form it may be. Or, I can change my one question to a series of several questions requiring yes-or-no answers: "Are the sides equal?" "Are all four angles equal?" and so on. It is possible to tell the number of yes-or-no questions that have to be asked by finding out how many possible answers there were to the first question. If the original query has four possible answers—*a*, *b*, *c*, and *d*—it will be necessary to ask two yes-or-no questions. First, "Is it either *a* or *b*?" If the answer is "No," it is apparent that the correct reply would be either *c* or *d*. If the answer is "Yes," then the right reply is either *a* or *b*. The second question, then, would be a choice between the two remaining possibilities. This can be shown mathematically,

$$2^2 = 2 \times 2 = 4$$

The mathematical concept of probability is also used in information theory. For instance, when a coin is tossed it can come up heads or tails, $+$ or $-$, 1 or 0. The probability that heads will come up—that 1 will appear—is always .5. On the average, heads will come up 50 per cent of the time. This probability does not change the more times the coin is tossed.

Let us take a communication system that transmits in the binary code. The probability that noise would interfere with any one signal is .5; in other words, about 50 per cent of the time a 1 might come through as a 0 or a 0 as a 1. Since the entire message is a series of 1's and 0's, it is clear that no message could be communicated.

But it is possible to use an error-correcting code. Suppose the following binary sequences of numbers were being transmitted: 10011010, 11101011, 1011. It would be possible to add one more binary digit to the end of each of the sequences as a part of an error-correcting code. If one added the number of 1's in each sequence and divided by 2, the remainder would be either 1 or 0, depending on whether the sum is an odd or even number. For example, in the first sequence the sum of the digits is 5. Five divided by 2 is 2 with a remainder of 1. So, a 1 would be added as the last number in order to make the sequence total an even number—in this case 6—and the number would become 100110101. In the second sequence, the sum is 6; and 6 divided by 2 is 3, with a remainder of 0. Thus, in the second number 0 would be added, and it would become 111010110. The third number would be 10111. It can be seen that when the error-correcting code was applied, the number of 1's in any sequence would always be even, that is, would always be divisible by 2 with a remainder of 0. If an error occurs in transmission, the number of ones will be odd and the error will be noticed.

The mathematical theory of information applies to the animal communication system as well as to radio, TV, and so on. Since the neuron transmits communications with an on-off, 1–0 pulse, it has already performed the first step and sends information in the binary code. There is noise, too, in the animal communication system. The EEG tape of an epileptic may show disturbances of normal brain-wave patterns, a kind of static that may interfere with the transmission of information. People who, because of certain neurological disorders, are unable to balance or walk a straight line may be suffering from an overwhelming amount of noise that interferes with the functioning of the nervous system and distorts the information the neurons transmit.

Information theory, too, like the other aspects of cybernetics, is applicable to self-regulating systems, whether they are mechanical or animal. What the mathematical theory of information tells us about telephone communication—it originated from work done at the Bell Telephone Laboratories—may reveal another aspect of the functioning of the human brain.

Throughout the history of life on this earth, living forms evolved from the simple to the more complex, as did societies. Now, man is faced with increasingly complex areas of knowledge and is searching to understand his own mind and the technology that that mind created. It is no longer possible to know most of what is known or to learn about almost everything. The time of specialization has come. But cybernetics seeks to find a single vocabulary and a single set of concepts to describe very different systems. Through cybernetics man will be able to find parallels and similarities among man, his machines, and his society. In this way, cybernetics is man's "steersman" to a new age.

9

New Age,
New Problems, New Hopes

A REVOLUTION brings with it change, upheaval, and, frequently, new social problems and structures. The cybernetic revolution presents modern man with far-reaching philosophical, economic, and social problems. Just as the weavers in France feared for their jobs when Jacquard introduced his punched cards, modern workers are faced with automation on a vast scale. Automation is the use in industry and technology of feedback control systems to operate automatically controlled manufacturing or operational systems. One of the advances of the first Industrial Revolution was the discovery that one man attempting to do all of the operations in the construction of a given item made fewer objects than a number of men each specializing in one operation. The American automobile pioneer Henry Ford (1863–1947), for example, realized this and, in the early years of the twentieth century, introduced the assembly line into the manufacturing of automobiles. Although various aspects of automation have long existed—the thermostat is an automated device—man is now faced with the automation of large parts of the industrial system.

Factory workers are finding that a machine can not only do their jobs, it can even do them better. Unskilled workmen are not the only part of the labor force to suffer from automation. The white-collar worker, who was either untouched by or whose jobs actually increased due to earlier technological advances, now finds that he, too, is being replaced by machines. The ability of electronic computers to calculate, record, and reason has meant that for many routine—and not so routine—office jobs, the machine is faster, cheaper, and more efficient than its human counterpart. For instance, many large corporations now handle inventory and shipment records through machines.

To some people this has meant that technological unemployment, the loss of jobs through automation and mechanization, is threatening mankind with new economic disasters. As unemployment increases, it is felt, the chances for another, more severe depression grow. They picture millions unable to find work and dependent on government and state aid. But this grim view of the future is not necessarily an accurate one. It comes in part from the age-old fear of the machine; men still look upon the "electronic brains" as Frankenstein monsters of the present, potentially demonic creations that may someday enslave mankind. Actually, there is no doubt that a serious problem does exist. As automation continues, jobs will disappear. On the other hand, jobs will also be created. The Second

Industrial Revolution has brought with it new industries and new opportunities for work on all levels. It is true that these new jobs require different training and a different education from earlier careers, but the modern worker, if he can adjust to these new demands, will also find his place in the new occupations that develop.

In this book the brain has been compared to the electronic computer. It may be useful to ask if one computer, the brain, has any advantages over the other, the electronic computer.

First, compare the amount of energy needed to operate the brain and that needed to run a computer. It has been calculated that the entire brain runs on less than 100 watts, while a machine with as great a capacity as the brain—assuming one could be built—would need at least one million times as much electrical power to continue operating.

But the computer is a faster worker than the brain. The advanced calculators are thousands upon thousands of times faster than the brain, and models yet to be built will probably be yet speedier.

Memory is of vital importance in "computer-type" operations. The number of bits of information that can be stored determines the ability of the system to do complex operations. The more bits stored, the more complex the calculations that can be made. In 1962, advanced electronic computers could store about 40,000 bits of information. Here, the brain shows its distinct advantages: although the number of bits stored is, of course, not known, it has been estimated at 10^{10}, or 10,000,000,000 bits.

The American neuropsychiatrist Dr. Warren McCulloch

has said that if a machine were built that could simulate the capacity of the human brain, it would have to be the size of a skyscraper; and all the electrical power supplied by Niagara Falls would be needed to run this mammoth machine, along with all the Falls' water to cool it. To quote Dr. McCulloch, "The brain is like a computing machine, but there is no computing machine like the brain."

Human beings may, however, not have even this superiority for long. Recent developments in electronic equipment, including Sceptron (see pages 73–74), an artificial nerve cell, have rapidly changed our ideas. Each Sceptron is 1/300 of a cubic inch in size. And this, say its manufacturers, means that it will soon be possible to make a calculator as complex as the human brain—with the same bit storage capacity—and package it in a desk-top unit.

There is one great and vitally significant distinction between human beings and machines. While electronic devices may think, "hunger" for electricity, and in other ways simulate animal and human behavior, men have drives, hungers, thirsts, and a complex existence of which the brain is a major, but not the entire, aspect. Human aspirations, hopes, and fears are not duplicated by electronic mechanisms, nor will they be as long as we continue to construct thinking machines whose function is only to think.

The use that man makes of automation, decision-making machines, and the other ramifications of cybernetics is dependent on man himself. As Norbert Wiener points out in his book *The Human Use of Human Beings*, mankind is confronted with two possibly destructive directions in which cybernetics could develop, influencing all of society. One is that machines that do not learn will be rigid and literal-minded in their approach to problems, interpreting their instructions in an obvious, inflexible way. The other is that man may find himself in the position of the Arab fisherman in *A Thousand and One Nights* who released the angry genie: machines that can learn and make decisions on the basis of their learning are not obligated to decide in ways that please or better humanity. Men cannot give machines responsibility over mankind; ultimate choices must always be made by and in favor of men.

APPENDIX
GLOSSARY
CHRONOLOGY
SELECTED BIBLIOGRAPHY
INDEX

Appendix: Truth Tables

THE DIGITAL COMPUTER's mathematical ability includes logical as well as arithmetical calculation. When a computer works with logic, it manipulates statements as if they were mathematical quantities. One way to see how the computer approaches logical problems is to look at some "truth tables." These are tables that use numbers to symbolize the yes-no (true-false) possibilities of statements. In the tables below, 1 means true and 0 means false. Two separate sets of statements are used. First, "If a lamp is plugged in (A) and the switch is turned on (B), then the light will go on (C)." In this form of statement both A and B have to be true for C to be true. A table can be made up using 1 and 0 to show that there are four possibilities: (1) A and B are false, so C is false; (2) A is true, but B is false, so C is false; (3) A is false, B is true, so C is still false; (4) A and B are both true, so C is true as well. In only one of them will C be true.

	A	B	C
(1)	o	o	o
(2)	1	o	o
(3)	o	1	o
(4)	1	1	1

This first statement might be called an "and" statement because A *and* B must be true for C to be true. A second kind might be called an "or" statement. If either A or B is true, C is true. For example: "Either by walking twenty blocks (A) or by riding on a bus for the same twenty blocks (B), I will get to my destination (C)." In this case, out of the four possibilities, three will allow C to be true.

A	B	C
o	o	o
1	o	1
o	1	1
1	1	1

It is possible to consider the wiring of an electrical circuit as representing either one of the two forms of statements. This can be demonstrated by setting up electrical circuits with a dry cell, two switches, and a light bulb. In the drawing the circuit on top has been wired so that both switches have to be closed for the bulb to light. The two switches are called "AND gates." But the circuit can be wired in a very different way so that either of the two switches can be closed and the other left open in order to turn on the light. These switches are called "OR gates."

But engineers have discovered an electronic bit of "presto-chango" that would shame even the best of magicians. With nothing up our sleeves and nothing concealed in the magic box, we take an AND gate, reverse the flow of the electrical current, and the AND gate is transformed into an OR gate. When current is reversed, it is equivalent to changing all the 0's to 1's and all the 1's to 0's. In order to see how this transformation works, take the first truth table—the AND table—and imagine a reversed current changing 0's to 1's and vice versa.

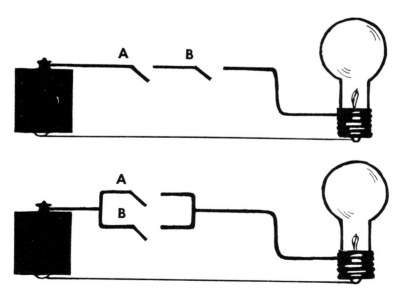

AND gate (top) and OR gate.

First Table			*First Table Reversed*		
A	*B*	*C*	*A*	*B*	*C*
0	0	0	1	1	1
1	0	0	0	1	1
0	1	0	1	0	1
1	1	1	0	0	0

Now, compare the reversed first table with the OR truth table. It is the same as the OR table read from bottom to top! The computer, using these binary digits, is able to store, calculate with, and decide certain logical problems by means of its electronic circuits.

Glossary

Alpha Rhythm—the typical flow of ten pulses of electricity per second from the brain of an adult at rest.

Analog Computer—a device used to measure the amount of a quantity in a given state and to note its variance. Such a device deals with systems as a whole rather than with individual parts of a system. See *digital computer*.

Anode—in the vacuum tube, a positively charged metallic element.

Atom—the smallest particle of an element to retain all the physical and chemical properties of that element.

Axon—the part of a nerve cell that transmits the output.

Base—the number used as the basis for a mathematical system.

Binary System—the language of electronic computers. A mathematical system with a base of 2.

Bionics—the science that studies the similarities and relationships between the machine and the brain; it is also concerned with the construction of machines that imitate certain aspects of life.

Bit—a binary digit; 1 or 0.

Black Box—a representation of a system that contains unknown components, but whose input and output can be observed.

Brain Wave—the pulse of electrical current transmitted by the brain. See *alpha rhythm*.

Calculator—see *computer*.

Cathode—in the vacuum tube, a source of negatively charged particles.

Closed System—a system that operates with interdependent parts and with no elements essential to the operation located outside the system.

Communication—the transmission of information from a sender to a receiver. It can be between man and man, man and machine, or between machine and machine.

Computer—any device that computes or calculates. See *analog computer* and *digital computer*.

Cortex—the area of the brain that is apparently the control center of the nervous system.

Cybernetics—the science that deals with control and communication in self-regulating systems, both animal and machine.

Decimal System—the most common mathematical system and the one used in modern Western civilizations; it has a base of 10.

Dendrite—a filament in a nerve cell that transmits the incoming electrical signal.

Deoxyribonucleic Acid (DNA)—the giant protein molecule containing the hereditary blueprint.

Digit—in the decimal system, any number from 0 through 9.

Digital Computer—a computer that uses the binary digits 1 and 0 to calculate quantity—how many of something there are—and to perform mathematical and logical operations.

Electricity—a flow of negatively charged particles, electrons; sometimes called "negative electricity."

Electrode—a tool with a pointed end capable of emitting electrical current.

Electron—an atomic particle carrying a negative charge.

Electroencephalograph (*EEG*)—a device used to register and record brain waves.

Electronic Computer—a calculating mechanism using electrical power. See *digital computer* and *analog computer*.

Electrophysiology—the science dealing with the study of animal electricity.

Elements—the basic substances of which the universe is made.

Feedback—the process in which some information produced by a system in response to stimuli (input) is fed back into the system in order to furnish it additional means of control and regulation. See *self-regulating system*.

Flip-Flop—two vacuum tubes so arranged that when one is on the other is off.

Grid—in the triode type of vacuum tube, an element placed between the cathode and the anode to control the flow of electrons.

Homeostasis—the tendency of an organism to maintain its internal equilibrium by compensating for disruptive stimuli.

Hypothalamus—a small area of the brain that operates as a control center for a number of body functions, such as temperature control.

Input—information fed into a system.

Ions—atomic particles, atoms, or molecules that can carry either a positive or a negative charge.

Magnetic Tape—tape on which small areas can be magnetized in one of two opposite directions; used in electronic computers for input, memory, and output operations.

Mathematical Logic—the use of mathematical symbols to represent language and its processes, in which these symbols are manipulated in accord with mathematical rules in order to determine whether or not a statement or a series of statements is true or false.

Memory—in man or machine, the storage and retention of information.

Memory Core—a doughnut-shaped piece of ferrite metal that can be used, when it is magnetized in one of two opposite directions, to store a bit of information.

Molecule—a group of atoms of one or more elements linked together to form a compound—the smallest part of the compound to retain its properties.

Neuron—a nerve cell, the basic component of the nervous system, composed of a central cell body with dendrites, filaments radiating from it, and an axon.

Neutron—a particle in the nucleus of an atom with no electrical charge.

Noise—anything that interferes with the transmission of a message.

Output—the reaction of an organism or a mechanism to a stimulus affecting the system.

Photoelectric Cell—a light-sensitive device that transforms lights into electrical impulses.

Program—a sequence of coded bits of information fed into a computer, giving it a plan of operation.

Programmer—a person who prepares and codes a program.

Proton—a particle in the nucleus of an atom with a positive electrical charge.

Reflex Action—an action that is the result of the effect of a stimulus or disturbance on the nervous system.

Ribonucleic Acid (RNA)—a heredity-related giant protein molecule.

Scientific Method—the procedure of logical, objective, and systematic study of physical phenomena.

Self-regulating System—a closed system that, operating through the feedback and intercommunication of its component parts, control itself.

Symbolic Logic—see *mathematical logic*.

Synapse—the point between nerve cells at which the the electrical current is transmitted from one cell to another.

Vacuum Tube—an enclosure, from which most of the air has been pumped, used to alter electrical current.

Chronology

1642   Pascal builds and uses his desk-top calculator.

1673   Leibniz exhibits his calculator, an improvement on that of Pascal.

1791   Galvani publishes a report of his researches in animal electricity.

1801   Jacquard introduces his loom, using punched cards to control the fabric pattern.

1817   Magendie discusses feedback and control in the animal system.

1823   Babbage begins works on the Difference Engine.

1833   Babbage abandons the Difference Engine to concentrate his efforts on the Analytical Engine.

1848   Helmholtz finds the speed with which a frog's nerve impulses are transmitted.

1854   Boole publishes *An Investigation of the Laws of Thought*.

1868   Maxwell publishes "The Theory of Governors," discussing control mechanisms.

1875 The first animal brain waves are recorded.

1914 Torres y Quevedo exhibits his machine capable of playing an end game of chess.

1927 Bush completes the Differential Analyzer, first successful large-scale electronic computer.

1929 Berger invents the electroencephalograph.

1932 Cannon issues the first detailed description of the phenomenon of homeostasis, and names it.

1938 Shannon initiates the mathematical theory of information with his paper, "A Symbolic Analysis of Relay and Switching Circuits."

1944 Eniac, the first electronic digital computer, is put into operation.

1948 Wiener publishes *Cybernetics or Control and Communication in the Animal and the Machine*

1948 Ashby constructs Homeostat.

1949 Shannon and Weaver publish an extension and crystallization of their 1938 work, A *Mathematical Theory of Communications.*

1950's During this decade rapid advances take place in miniaturization, technology of computers, programing, and so forth. Rapid strides in increased memory storage, speed of operations, and flexibility of operation broaden the areas in which computers can be used.

1959 Artificial neurons are constructed.

1960 Air Force calls the first bionics conference, naming this new science.

1963 Increased complexity and miniaturization of electrical equipment proceeds.

Selected Bibliography

BOOKS

Adler, Irving, *Thinking Machines*. New York: Signet Science Library, 1962.

Berkeley, Edmund C., *Giant Brains*. New York: Science Editions, Inc., 1961.

Cannon, Walter B., *The Wisdom of the Body*. New York: Norton, 1939.

Editors of *Scientific American*, *Automatic Control*, a Scientific American Book. New York: Simon and Schuster, 1955.

Galambos, Robert, *Nerves and Muscles*. New York: Anchor Books, 1962.

Guilbaud, G. T., *What is Cybernetics?* New York: Grove Press, Inc., 1960.

Halacy, D. S., Jr., *Computers: The Machine We Think With*. New York and Evanston: Harper & Row, 1962.

Pask, Gordon, *An Approach to Cybernetics*. New York: Harper & Brothers, 1961.

Pavlov, I. P., *Conditioned Reflexes*. New York: Dover Publications, Inc., 1960.

Pfeiffer, John, *The Human Brain*. New York: Harper & Brothers, 1955.
———, *The Thinking Machine*, Philadelphia and New York: J. B. Lippincott Company, 1962.
Neumann, John von, *The Computer and the Brain*. New Haven and London: Yale University Press, 1958.
———, "The General and Logical Theory of Automata" in *Machines, Music, and Puzzles*, edited by James R. Newman. New York: Simon and Schuster, 1956.
Reichenbach, Hans, *Elements of Symbolic Logic*. New York: The Macmillan Co., 1947.
Shannon, Claude, "A Chess-Playing Machine" in *Machines, Music, and Puzzles*, edited by James R. Newman. New York: Simon and Schuster, 1956.
——— and Weaver, W., *The Mathematical Theory of Communication*. Urbana: The University of Illinois Press, 1949.
Sluckin, W., *Minds and Machines*. Baltimore, Md.: Penguin Books, 1954.
Turing, A. M., "Can a Machine Think?" in *Machines, Music, and Puzzles*, edited by James R. Newman. New York: Simon and Schuster, 1956.
Walter, Grey, *The Living Brain*. New York: W. W. Norton and Co., 1953.
Wiener, Norbert, *Cybernetics: or Control and Communication in the Animal and the Machine*. Revised edition. New York: John Wiley & Sons, Inc., 1961.
——— *The Human Use of Human Beings: Cybernetics and Society*. Revised edition. New York: Anchor Books, 1954.

ARTICLES IN PERIODICALS

"A New American Poet Speaks: The Works of A. B." *Horizon*, Vol. 4, no. 5, May 1962. Pp. 96–99.
Ashby, W. Ross, "Design for a Brain." *Electronic Engineering*, Vol. 20, 1948.

Balandie, Leo S., "Sceptron: A Sound-Operated Fiber-Optic 'Brain Cell.'" *Electronics World,* March, 1963. Pp. 36–37, 77.

Gilmore, Ken, "Bionic Computers." *Electronics World,* March, 1963. Pp. 25–28, 63–64.

Peterson, W. Wesley, "Error Correcting Codes." *Scientific American,* Vol. 206, no. 2, February 1962. Pp. 96–108.

———— "Problems, Too, Have Problems." *Fortune,* October 1961. Pp. 144–148, 158–168.

Walter, Grey, "An Electromechanical 'Animal.'" *Discovery II,* March 1950. P. 90.

Index

ABOUT THE AUTHOR

Corinne Jacker, a former science teacher, is now a science editor with a major New York publishing company. She was born in Chicago and attended Stanford University in Palo Alto, California, and Northwestern University in Evanston, Illinois. Miss Jacker has also had plays produced off-Broadway and on television, and her poems have appeared in literary journals.